CALIFORNIA

Interactive Reading Notepad: Inquiry Companion

ECONOMICS

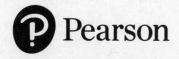 Pearson

Acknowledgments

Grateful acknowledgment is made to the following for copyrighted material:

Images:
Cover: Oxford/Getty Images

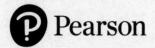

ISBN-13: 978-1-41-828670-5
ISBN-10:   1-41-828670-2

Contents

California Economics: Principles in Action
Interactive Reading Notepad: Inquiry Companion

Lesson 1.1 Scarcity

Key Terms

needs	entrepreneur
wants	factors of production
goods	land
services	labor
scarcity	capital
economics	physical capital
shortage	human capital

Academic Vocabulary

Essential: necessary; cannot be done without

Available: obtainable

Fertile: capable of growing crops

Technical: related to a particular technology

Lesson Objectives

1 **Explain** why scarcity and choice are problems that every society faces.

2 **Summarize** how entrepreneurs fuel economic growth.

3 **Describe** the three economic factors of production and the differences between physical and human capital.

4 **Explain** how scarcity affects the factors of production.

Scarcity Means Making Choices: Text

1. **Categorize** What are two examples of goods and two examples of services? (Do not cite examples provided in the lesson.)

2. **Draw Inferences** What is an example of the kinds of choices that a business would have to make because of scarcity?

3. **Compare and Contrast** According to the lesson, scarcity is a problem that all societies face. Is the same true of shortages? Why or why not?

4. **Summarize** Use this chart to summarize the reading.

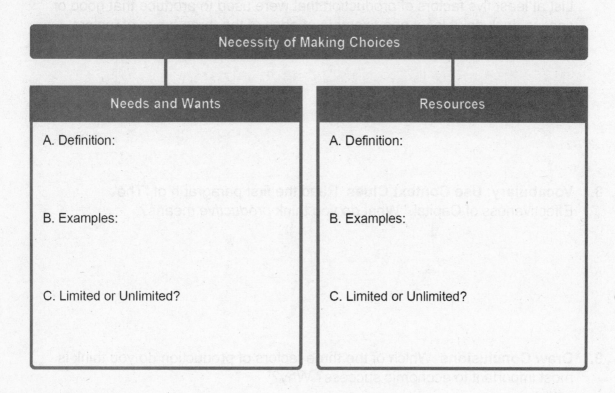

Necessity of Making Choices

Needs and Wants	Resources
A. Definition:	A. Definition:
B. Examples:	B. Examples:
C. Limited or Unlimited?	C. Limited or Unlimited?

Entrepreneurs Use Factors of Production: Text

5. **Assess an Argument** Jean-Baptiste Say thought that entrepreneurs should be considered a fourth factor of production. Do you agree or not? Explain your reasoning.

6. **Draw Inferences** What land resources are used by a company that produces movies?

Interactive Reading Notepad • Lesson 1.1

7. **Analyze Interactions** Think of a good or service that you consumed today. List at least five factors of production that were used to produce that good or service. Include at least one example of each of the three types of factors—land, labor, and capital.

8. **Vocabulary: Use Context Clues** Read the first paragraph of "The Effectiveness of Capital." What do you think *productive* means?

9. **Draw Conclusions** Which of the three factors of production do you think is most important to economic success? Why?

All Resources Are Scarce: Text

10. **Summarize** How does scarcity force people to make economic choices?

11. **Analyze Interactions** Describe how scarcity of time, money, or resources affected a recent economic decision you made.

Lesson 1.2 Opportunity Cost and Trade-Offs

Key Terms

trade-off

guns or butter

opportunity cost

thinking at the margin

cost/benefit analysis

marginal cost

marginal benefit

Academic Vocabulary

Intangibles: assets that are not capable of being touched; abstract qualities, such as enjoyment

Rein: to check, slow, or stop as if pulling on reins

Lesson Objectives

1 **Identify** why every decision involves trade-offs.

2 **Explain** the concept of opportunity cost.

3 **Describe** how people make decisions by thinking at the margin.

Making Decisions: Text

1. **Identify Cause and Effect** Why does every decision involve a trade-off?

2. **Paraphrase** Use your own words to describe the trade-off known as "guns or butter."

Opportunity Cost: Text

3. **Vocabulary: Use Context Clues** Read the first paragraph of "Opportunity Cost." What do you think the word *alternative* means? How does it relate to opportunity cost?

4. **Categorize** Refer to Karen's Decision-Making Grid in "Opportunity Cost." Which benefits are intangible? Which benefits are measurable?

5. **Draw Conclusions** How might intangible benefits affect Karen's decision?

Thinking at the Margin: Text

6. **Paraphrase** Consider what the word *margin* means. Then, explain in your own words what it means to "think at the margin."

7. **Determine Central Ideas** What are the two main parts of a cost/benefit analysis? How are they used to make a decision?

Lesson 1.3 Production Possibilities Curves

Key Terms

production possibilities curve   underutilization

production possibilities frontier   law of increasing costs

efficiency

Academic Vocabulary

Capacity: the ability to hold, contain, or absorb

Lesson Objectives

1 **Interpret** a production possibilities curve.

2 **Explain** how production possibilities curves show efficiency, growth, and cost.

3 **Explain** why a country's production possibilities depend on its resources and technology.

Production Possibilities Curves: Text

1. **Analyze Data** Look at Figure 1.3, showing production possibilities for watermelons and shoes. What keeps Capeland from producing 21 million tons of watermelons each year as well as 15 million pairs of shoes?

2. **Apply Concepts** Many countries produce a single good upon which much of their economy depends. That good might be coffee or wool or oil. How might a production possibilities curve help economists in such a country determine how to diversify their economy?

Interactive Reading Notepad • Lesson 1.3

Changing Production Possibilities: Text

3. **Summarize** As you read "Changing Production Possibilities," use this graphic organizer to record details about the production possibilities curve.

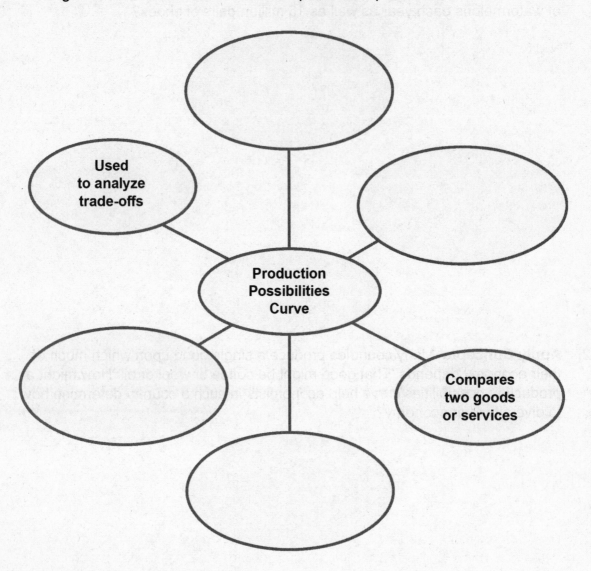

Used
to analyze
trade-offs

Production
Possibilities
Curve

Compares
two goods
or services

4. **Draw Conclusions** An inventor found a new way to produce more steel from each ton of her country's iron ore. How would a production possibilities curve reflect the application of that discovery to the country's production of steel cookware? Why?

5. **Compare and Contrast** The leader of Capeland gave all workers a month-long vacation from work to celebrate a national holiday. Would this show up on the production possibilities curve as underutilization or as a shift of the production possibilities frontier to the left? Explain.

6. **Cause and Effect** If a country chose to produce twice as many wooden chairs as before, how would that affect its production of wooden tables? How would the law of increasing costs apply to the chairs?

7. **Analyze Interactions** Capeland's workers made shoes by hand. This year, Capeland Shoe Company bought 100 computerized shoe-sewing machines. At the same time, the government funded a shoe-making course at Capeland Community College. Why did it make economic sense for the government to fund the course?

Lesson 2.1 The Three Key Economic Questions

Key Terms

economic system

factor payment

profit

safety net

standard of living

innovation

traditional economy

Academic Vocabulary

Equity: fairness

Prioritize: arrange in order of importance

Lesson Objectives

1 **Identify** the three basic economic questions that all societies must answer.

2 **Describe** the economic goals that determine how a society answers the three economic questions.

3 **Define** the characteristics of a traditional economy.

Three Basic Economic Questions: Reading

1. **Categorize** As you read "Three Basic Economic Questions," use this graphic organizer to list the three questions and provide at least two examples that illustrate each. The examples need not come from the lesson.

Three Basic Economic Questions	Examples
1.	
2.	
3.	

2. **Vocabulary: Use Context Clues** Under "Who Consumes the Goods and Services That Are Produced," use context clues to come up with a definition of the word *values*.

Economic Goals of Society: Reading

3. **Draw Inferences** How does the introduction of robots into an automobile factory illustrate the economic goal of efficiency?

4. **Draw Conclusions** A key innovation during the Industrial Revolution was the steam engine. How did the steam engine contribute to the growth of the textile, or cloth-making, industry?

5. **Explain an Argument** In a society that favors economic equity over economic freedom, who would benefit? Explain.

6. **Distinguish Among Fact, Opinion, and Reasoned Judgment** People in societies with traditional economies tend to rely on established technologies, have access to limited goods, and lack modern conveniences, but they love what they do for work. What part of the preceding statement is an opinion? Explain your answer.

7. **Cite Evidence** Which is the more important economic goal for society in a traditional economy, equity or growth? Cite evidence to support your answer.

Lesson 2.2 Free Markets

Key Terms

market	Adam Smith
specialization	self-interest
free market economy	incentive
household	competition
firm	price competition
factor market	non-price competition
product market	consumer sovereignty

Academic Vocabulary

Concentration: intense, narrow focus

Self-sufficiency: the ability to provide for one's own needs

Synonym: word that, relative to another word, has the same meaning

Motivating: causing a particular response or behavior

Lesson Objectives

1 **Explain** why markets exist.

2 **Analyze** a circular flow model of a free market economy.

3 **Describe** how self-interest and competition lead to the self-regulating nature of the marketplace.

4 **Identify** the advantages of a free market economy.

Why Do Markets Exist? Reading

1. **Draw Conclusions** Think about something you purchased recently. Assume you had to work for the money you paid for the item. Would it have taken you more work to get the money or to make the item yourself? How does this show the importance of markets?

2. **Analyze Interactions** Read the second paragraph of "The Role of Specialization." Many people grow their own fruits and vegetables. Explain whether this makes economic sense. If not, why do think people might do it?

Elements of a Free Market Economy: Reading

3. **Compare and Contrast** Think of an example of a product or service you buy for which you have lots of choices. Now think of an example of a product or service you buy for which you have few or no choices. What are the differences between the markets for those two items?

4. **Use Visual Information** Read the section "Factor and Product Markets" and review Figure 2.4, "Circular Flow Model of a Market Economy." How do households supply firms with land, labor, and capital? Provide an example of each.

How Markets Self-Regulate: Reading

5. **Evaluate Explanations** Read the quotation from Adam Smith about how self-interest motivates our economic interactions. Now describe an example of an economic interaction you have had and how your self-interest motivated you. Can you think of an example of an economic interaction in which you did not put your own self-interest first?

6. **Determine Central Ideas** Consider the example of shirt makers in the section "Incentives and Competition." Suppose that all but one of the manufacturers went out of business. What might happen to shirt prices if there were only one manufacturer? What might happen to the quality and number of choices? Why?

7. **Determine Central Ideas** Think about Adam Smith's concept of the "invisible hand." Explain in your own words what this is and how it works in a free market economy.

Advantages of a Free Market: Reading

8. **Vocabulary: Determine Meaning** One of the advantages of a free market is consumer sovereignty. Why do consumers hold such power in a free market system? Give a specific example to support your answer.

9. **Summarize** What are the characteristics of a free market economy? Use this graphic organizer to record the major characteristics of a free market. Add more ovals if necessary.

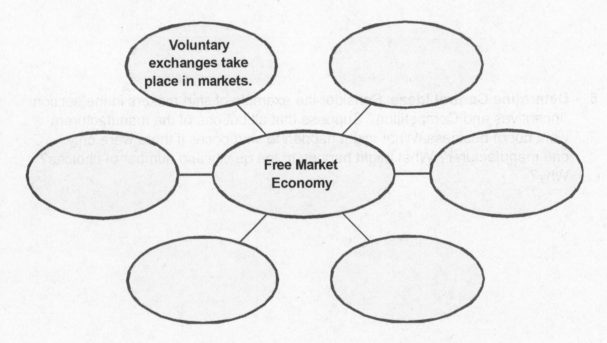

Interactive Reading Notepad • Lesson 2.2

Interactive Reading Notepad

Lesson 2.3 Centrally Planned Economies

Key Terms

centrally planned economy   communism

command economy   authoritarian

socialism

Academic Vocabulary

Distribute: to spread or pass out something

Coexist: to exist at the same time

Exploitation: to use someone or something for your own gain

Prestige: a positive reputation

Lesson Objectives

1 **Describe** how a centrally planned economy is organized.

2 **Distinguish** between socialism and communism.

3 **Analyze** the use of central planning in the Soviet Union and China.

4 **Identify** the disadvantages of a centrally planned economy.

The Features of Central Planning: Reading

1. **Summarize** As you read "The Features of Central Planning," use this graphic organizer to summarize the main features and disadvantages of a centrally planned economy.

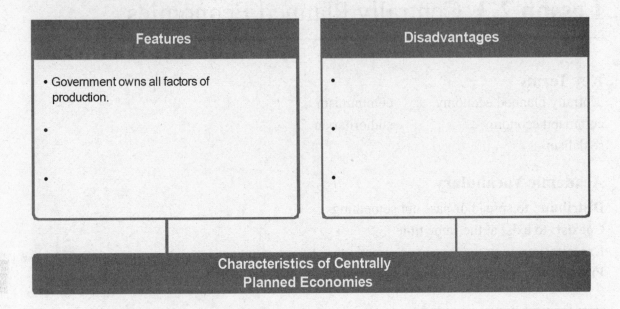

Features	Disadvantages
• Government owns all factors of production. • •	• • •

Characteristics of Centrally Planned Economies

2. **Determine Central Ideas** What method do centrally planned economies generally rely upon to control labor?

3. **Summarize** Explain why each of the following goals is difficult to achieve in a centrally planned economy: (a) economic freedom, (b) economic growth.

How Socialism and Communism Differ: Reading

4. Cite Evidence What makes Sweden an example of "market socialism"?

5. Draw Conclusions Read the quotation from Marx taken from *The Communist Manifesto* and the description of Marx's basic beliefs. Then explain why Marx believed that labor was more important than capital.

6. Generate Explanations Why do you think all communist governments have been authoritarian in nature?

Two Communist Economies: Reading

7. Identify Steps in a Process What were Stalin's goals for the Soviet economy, and how did he try to achieve them?

8. **Cite Evidence** (a) What was the benefit of the Soviet decision to concentrate on heavy industry? (b) What was the opportunity cost of this decision? Who paid it?

9. **Identify Cause and Effect** Why did the Chinese government institute new economic policies in the 1970s? What was the result?

Disadvantages of Central Planning: Reading

10. **Summarize** How is economic freedom undermined in centrally planned economies?

11. **Explain an Argument** Why is economic growth harder to achieve in a command economy than in a free market economy?

12. **Assess an Argument** Central planning is supposed to help achieve economic equity in society. Do you think this argument has merit, based on results?

13. **Cite Evidence** What strong evidence exists that centrally planned economies have not generally served the needs of countries?

Lesson 2.4 Mixed Economies

Key Terms

laissez faire

private property

mixed economy

economic transition

privatization

intellectual property

Academic Vocabulary

Element: component or feature of a complex whole

Doctrine: belief or principle central to a philosophy

Prioritize: to rank things according to their relative importance or urgency

Substantial: significant; sizeable and meaningful

Lesson Objectives

1 **Explain** the rise of mixed economic systems.

2 **Explain** how government actions affect a circular flow model of a mixed economy.

3 **Compare** the mixed economies of various nations along a continuum between centrally planned and free market systems.

4 **Describe** the role of free enterprise in the United States economy.

The Reasons for Mixed Economies: Reading

1. **Vocabulary: Determine Meaning of Words** Read the third paragraph of "The Reasons for Mixed Economies." What do you think the word *inherent* means?

2. **Draw Conclusions** What do you think may be some of the inherent reasons why nations today do not have pure free market economies?

3. **Make Comparisons** Sweden is an example of a country that has high tax rates on those with high incomes and redistributes that income to others. Where do you think Sweden would be in relation to the United States on the continuum of mixed economies?

4. **Evaluate Explanations** Why would the government want to be involved in the economy to ensure competition?

Circular Flow Model of a Mixed Economy: Reading

5. **Use Visual Information** Look at the diagram of the circular flow in a mixed economy. Suppose a state government wants to buy some land from various private owners to build a new state office building. Where would that exchange fit in the circular flow model?

6. **Draw Inferences** Do business firms benefit in any way from transfer payments? Explain.

Mixed Economies Today: Reading

7. **Compare and Contrast** As you read "Mixed Economies Today" as well as the rest of this lesson, use this graphic organizer to record characteristics of free market and command systems present in the mixed economies in the world today.

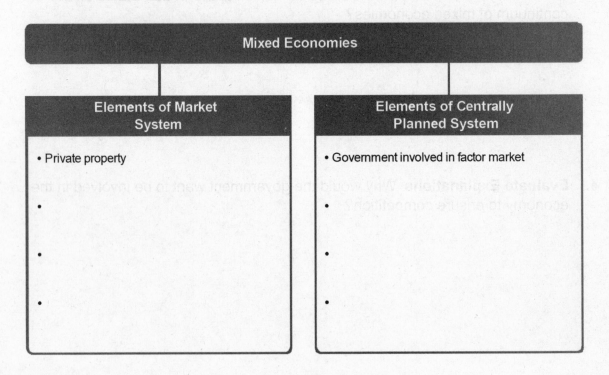

Mixed Economies	
Elements of Market System	**Elements of Centrally Planned System**
• Private property	• Government involved in factor market
•	•
•	•
•	•

8. **Cite Evidence** In North Korea, who buys most of the labor in the factor market? Cite evidence from the text to support your answer.

9. **Draw Inferences** Can an economy make the transition from a free market to a command system? If so, would privatization be involved? Why or why not?

The Economy of the United States: Reading

10. **Explain an Argument** What economic goals do you think those who want more government regulation are emphasizing? What goals are those who want less government regulation emphasizing?

Lesson 2.5 Benefits of Free Enterprise

Key Terms

profit motive

open opportunity

legal equality

private property rights

free contract

voluntary exchange

interest group

patriotism

eminent domain

public interest

public disclosure laws

Academic Vocabulary

Persistence: the quality of continuing despite problems or opposition

Dynamic: a force leading to change or growth

Disclosure: the act of making something known to the public

Implement: to put into effect

Lesson Objectives

1 **Explain** the basic characteristics of the U.S. free enterprise system.

2 **Describe** the role of the consumer and the entrepreneur in the American economy.

3 **Identify** the protections in the U.S. Constitution that underlie free enterprise.

4 **Describe** the role of government in the U.S. free enterprise system.

Basic Characteristics of Free Enterprise: Reading

1. **Categorize** As you read "Basic Characteristics of Free Enterprise," use this graphic organizer to categorize the characteristics and benefits of free enterprise.

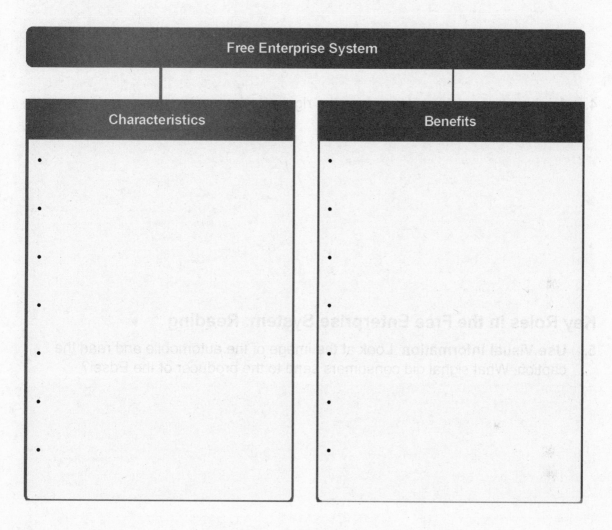

2. **Draw Inferences** What characteristic of the free enterprise system allows individuals to paint stripes or stars or polka dots on their cars?

Interactive Reading Notepad • Lesson 2.5

3. **Summarize** How does competition regulate the free market?

4. **Analyze Interactions** How does the right of voluntary exchange promote competition?

Key Roles in the Free Enterprise System: Reading

5. **Use Visual Information** Look at the image of the automobile and read the caption. What signal did consumers send to the producer of the Edsel?

6. **Draw Inferences** What kind of person makes a good entrepreneur? List at least two personality traits of a successful entrepreneur.

Economic Freedom and the Constitution: Reading

7. **Vocabulary: Use Context Clues** The word *eminent* can mean "having a position of superiority." The word *domain* can mean "rights to the ownership of land." Use these meanings to explain why the government can take someone's private property.

8. **Use Visual Information** What does the cartoon suggest about property rights versus the government's rights of eminent domain?

9. **Draw Conclusions** Why do you think the Constitution was amended in 1913 to allow Congress to tax incomes directly?

The Limited Role of Government in the Marketplace: Reading

10. **Determine Central Ideas** Look at the photo of the automobile dealership. How do consumers benefit from public disclosure laws related to buying a car?

11. Cite Evidence to support the idea that government acts to promote the public interest.

12. Assess an Argument Highly regulated industries have argued that government rules and regulations stifle competition, resulting in prices that are unnecessarily high. Does this argument make sense? Why or why not?

Lesson 2.6 Supporting Economic Growth

Key Terms

macroeconomics
microeconomics
gross domestic product (GDP)
business cycle
referendum

obsolescence
patent
copyright
work ethic

Academic Vocabulary

Contraction: when something declines or gets smaller

Fluctuations: a shifting back and forth or up and down

Accommodation: something supplied to meet a need

Lesson Objectives

1 **Explain** why the government tracks and seeks to influence business cycles.

2 **Analyze** how the government promotes economic strength and stability.

3 **Describe** the factors that increase productivity.

Tracking the Economy: Reading

1. **Analyze Interactions** Read the third paragraph of "Tracking the Economy." Using the terms *macroeconomic* and *microeconomic*, explain the economic relationship between a nation and the firms and households that are in that nation.

2. **Draw Conclusions** If you pay attention to the news, you probably hear a lot about national economic data such as unemployment or gross domestic product (GDP). If you have a steady job, why should you care how the rest of the country is doing?

Encouraging Economic Strength: Reading

3. **Summarize** How does the government encourage economic growth and stability? Use this graphic organizer to record the key ideas from this reading.

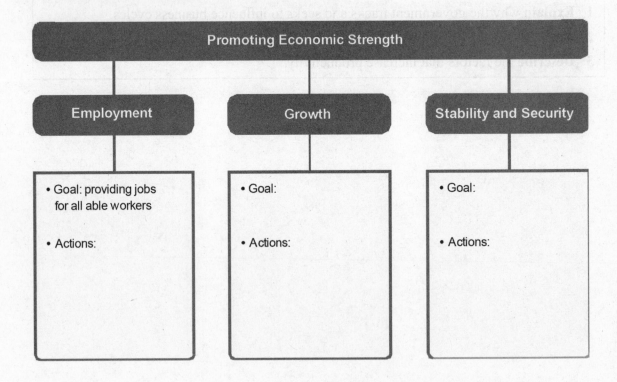

Promoting Economic Strength

Employment
- Goal: providing jobs for all able workers
- Actions:

Growth
- Goal:
- Actions:

Stability and Security
- Goal:
- Actions:

Interactive Reading Notepad • Lesson 2.6

4. **Identify Cause and Effect** Read the section "Stability." Suppose you own a business that sells hot dog buns and other bread products to restaurants. What would happen if the price of the wheat that is used to make buns went up? Trace the economic impact from the wheat farmer to the flour mill to your business to the restaurant and beyond.

5. **Draw Inferences** Question 4 dealt with a specific example of how prices rise. What would happen if many businesses all across the country found themselves in the same situation?

Productivity and the Role of Technology: Reading

6. **Draw Conclusions** Read the section "Technological Progress." Suppose you own a factory that makes something you like, such as guitars or shoes. Hundreds of people work at your factory, assembling products, packaging and shipping products, and doing many other jobs. One day you install a robotic system that replaces half your workforce. The new system saves money and increases your profits, but over 100 people lose their jobs. Is that good for the economy or not? Explain your answer.

7. **Draw Conclusions** Consider the example of NASA in the section "Encouraging Innovation." When NASA was founded in 1958, establishing the space program was something only the government could do. Now, private companies routinely fly cargo and even passengers into space. Why do these private companies owe their existence to NASA and the space programs of other countries?

8. **Explain an Argument** Copyright law is meant to ensure that the people who create a work, such as a book, movie, or song, profit from it. Why do you think it is necessary to have laws to protect creative works of this sort?

Lesson 2.7 Public Goods and Externalities

Key Terms

public good

public sector

private sector

infrastructure

free rider

market failure

externality

poverty threshold

welfare

Academic Vocabulary

Impractical: not easily or efficiently achieved

Scenario: a sequence of events

Lesson Objectives

1 **Identify** examples of public goods.

2 **Analyze** market failures.

3 **Evaluate** how the government allocates some resources by managing externalities.

Public Goods: Reading

1. **Compare and Contrast** What is the difference between private goods and public goods? Explain the difference using examples.

2. **Draw Inferences** Why would a private firm be able to charge a very high admission fee if it owned Yellowstone National Park?

3. **Cite Evidence** to explain why infrastructure is a public good.

4. **Determine Central Ideas** How does an analysis of costs and benefits explain why an expensive project, such as a highway, gets produced as a public good, not a private good?

Market Failures: Reading

5. **Identify Cause and Effect** What two main criteria must be present to avoid market failure?

6. **Assess an Argument** Market failure proves that the free enterprise system does not work. Is this statement accurate? Why or why not?

Externalities: Reading

7. **Categorize** What might be one positive externality and one negative externality resulting from the establishment of a trucking company in a neighborhood?

8. **Draw Inferences** When chemicals from a paper mill seep into a waterway and a town downstream pays to clean them up, why is that considered a market failure?

9. **Paraphrase** Use your own words to paraphrase the debate among economists over dealing with negative externalities in a free market.

The Poverty Problem: Reading

10. **Determine Central Ideas** Why does the poverty threshold vary from year to year?

11. **Identify Cause and Effect** Why might income redistribution discourage productivity?

Lesson 3.1 Fundamentals of Demand

Key Terms

demand

law of demand

substitution effect

income effect

demand schedule

market demand schedule

demand curve

Academic Vocabulary

Alternative: an available choice

Vertical: running up and down

Horizontal: running side to side

Lesson Objectives

1 **Understand** how the law of demand explains the effects of price on quantity demanded.

2 **Describe** how the substitution effect and the income effect influence decisions.

3 **Explore** a demand schedule for an individual and a market.

4 **Interpret** a demand graph using demand schedules.

Demand: Text

1. **Draw Inferences** Read the definition of *demand* presented in the section "Demand." Why do you think both of these factors must be present in order to have true demand?

2. **Vocabulary: Determine Meaning** Read the quote from Professor Henderson in the section "The Law of Demand." What do you think Henderson means when he says that "on this law is built almost the whole edifice of economics"? What is the meaning of the word *edifice* in this context?

3. **Compare and Contrast** After reading the sections "The Substitution Effect" and "The Income Effect," compare and contrast the substitution effect and the income effect.

The Demand Schedule: Text

4. **Compare and Contrast** Look at Figure 3.1. How are individual and market demand schedules similar? How are they different?

5. **Determine Central Ideas** Read the sections "Understanding Demand" and "Market Demand Schedules." Which do you think would be most important to the owner of a business?

The Demand Graph: Text

6. **Vocabulary: Use Context Clues** Read the first paragraph under "The Demand Graph." What do you think the phrase *graphic representation* means?

7. **Vocabulary: Determine Meaning** What is the relationship between the words *curve* and *graph* in this discussion about demand graphs?

8. **Summarize** Complete this table based on what you have read in this lesson.

Demand		
	As the price of a good goes down…	As the price of a good goes up…
Law of demand		
Substitution effect		
Income effect		

Lesson 3.2 Shifts in Demand

Key Terms

ceteris paribus   complement

normal good   substitute

inferior good   nonprice determinant

demographics

Academic Vocabulary

Assumption: a belief or idea taken to be true

Expectation: a belief that an event or development will occur in the future

Generic: not having a brand name

Lesson Objectives

1 **Explain** the difference between a change in quantity demanded and a shift in the demand curve.

2 **Identify** non-price determinants that create changes in demand and can cause a shift in the demand curve.

3 **Summarize** examples of how a change in demand for one good can affect demand for a related good.

Changes in Demand: Text

1. **Vocabulary: Determine the Meaning** What does *ceteris paribus* mean? Restate the meaning in your own words.

2. **Cite Evidence** Read the first paragraph under "Changes in Demand." Was the person's change in demand for a burger in this situation based on price or on some other factor?

The Non-Price Determinants of Demand: Text

3. **Summarize** As you read through this lesson, complete this web diagram about what causes demand curves to shift.

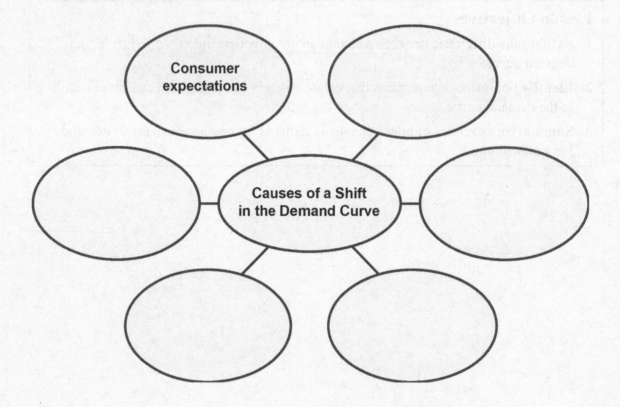

Interactive Reading Notepad • Lesson 3.2

4. **Categorize** What are non-price determinants, and why are they given that name? Give some examples.

5. **Identify Cause and Effect** After reading the section "Changes in Income," explain how changes in income affect the demand for normal goods.

6. **Use Visual Information** Review the map "States with Tax Holidays." Note which states offer tax holidays. How do you think tax holidays affect demand?

7. **Draw Inferences** Think about normal goods and inferior goods. Give an example of normal and inferior goods that are also substitutes.

Lesson 3.3 Elasticity of Demand

Key Terms

elasticity of demand   unitary elastic

inelastic   total revenue

elastic

Academic Vocabulary

Dramatically: in a way or to an extent that draws attention

Drastically: in an extreme or exaggerated way

Precise: exact

Relatively: in relation or comparison to something else

Lesson Objectives

1 **Explain** how to calculate elasticity of demand.

2 **Identify** factors that affect elasticity of demand.

3 **Explain** how firms use elasticity and revenue to make decisions.

Elasticity Defined: Text

1. **Use Visual Information** Use Figure 3.4 to answer the following: If the cost of gasoline increases from $3.00 per gallon to $4.00 per gallon and the quantity demanded decreases from 12 gallons to 10 gallons, would the demand be elastic or inelastic?

2. **Determine Central Ideas** Read the section "Price Range." Why do you think people are more willing to pay 50 percent more for a product that increases in price from 75 cents to $1.00 than a product that increases from $5.00 to $7.50, also an increase of 50 percent?

3. **Vocabulary: Use Context Clues** Look at the word *unitary*. Based on the definition of the term *unitary elastic* and the context, what do you think this term means?

Factors Affecting Elasticity: Text

4. **Categorize** If a person is willing to give up her yearly two-week cruise in the Caribbean due to a price increase, her action illustrates which factor affecting elasticity? Explain your answer.

Interactive Reading Notepad • Lesson 3.3

5. **Categorize** Which factor affecting elasticity explains why a person may continue to purchase gasoline even though the price rises sharply?

6. **Analyze Sequence** Read the section "Change Over Time," and explain the process by which time affects elasticity.

How Elasticity Affects Revenue: Text

7. **Identify Cause and Effect** Complete the graphic organizer to illustrate what happens to revenues when the elasticity of demand and change in price are considered.

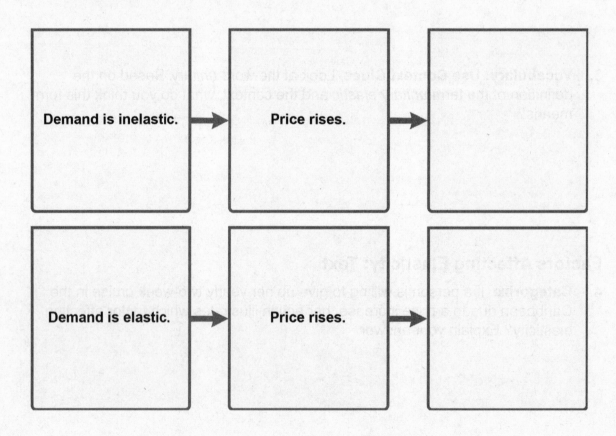

Demand is inelastic. ➡ Price rises. ➡

Demand is elastic. ➡ Price rises. ➡

8. **Use Visual Information** Look at Figure 3.7. What would total revenue be if the price went to $7 a slice but demand fell to just 25 slices?

9. **Determine Central Ideas** Read "How Elasticity Affects Pricing Policies." Explain why a business owner needs to understand elasticity of demand for his or her good or service when considering price changes.

Lesson 3.4 Fundamentals of Supply

Key Terms

supply	market supply schedule
law of supply	supply curve
quantity supplied	market supply curve
supply schedule	elasticity of supply
variable	

Academic Vocabulary

Govern: to control or regulate

Generate: to create or make happen

Yield: to produce in return for some investment of labor, money

---

Lesson Objectives

1 **Understand** how the law of supply explains the effect of price on quantity supplied.

2 **Interpret** a supply schedule and a supply graph.

3 **Examine** the relationship between elasticity of supply and time.

The Effect of Price on Supply: Text

1. **Paraphrase** Read the section "Suppliers Follow the Law of Supply," and then state the law of supply in your own words.

2. **Cite Evidence** Read the section "The Effect of Price on Number of Suppliers." What support does the reading give for the idea that the music industry frequently sees a pattern of sharp increases and decreases in supply in response to trends?

3. **Draw Inferences** The reading says that the relative ease with which entrepreneurs can enter and leave markets is a benefit of the free enterprise system of the United States. Could the same statement be made about a country with a command economy? Why or why not? What implications does that have for the law of supply in that country?

Understanding Supply Schedules: Text

4. **Draw Inferences** Look at Figure 3.8. Why is there no quantity supplied at a price less than $1 per slice?

Interactive Reading Notepad • Lesson 3.4

5. **Determine Central Ideas** Read the section "Changes in the Quantity Supplied." Why does the entrepreneur increase or decrease supply in response to price increases or decreases?

6. **Compare and Contrast** Why are the supply curve and the market supply curve the same except for the quantity supplied?

7. **Compare and Contrast** Look at Figure 3.10, and compare it to Figure 3.2 in Lesson 1. How does a supply curve differ from a demand curve, and how is the difference related to increases in price?

Elasticity of Supply: Text

8. **Identify Cause and Effect** Read the last paragraph under the heading "Elasticity of Supply." Would a lawn care business have elastic or inelastic supply in the short term? Explain your answer.

9. Explain an Argument Read the section "Elasticity of Supply Over a Longer Time." How does the reading explain that elasticity of supply tends to increase over time?

Lesson 3.5 Costs of Production

Key Terms

marginal product of labor	total cost
increasing marginal returns	marginal cost
diminishing marginal returns	marginal revenue
negative marginal return	average cost
fixed cost	operating cost
variable cost	

Academic Vocabulary

Rational: using logical, clear thinking

Facility: a building or structure that serves a specific purpose

Lesson Objectives

1 **Explain** how businesses decide how much labor to hire in order to produce a certain level of output.

2 **Analyze** the production costs of a business.

3 **Explain** how a business chooses to set output.

4 **Identify** the factors that a firm must consider before shutting down an unprofitable business.

Labor and Output: Text

1. **Summarize** As you read, complete the graphic organizer with information about the concepts and goals that businesses must keep in mind when managing labor and setting output.

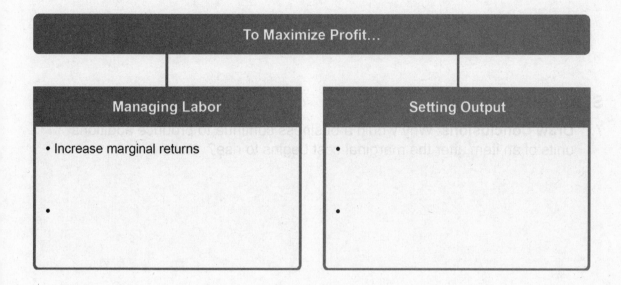

To Maximize Profit...

Managing Labor
- Increase marginal returns
-

Setting Output
-

2. **Identify Cause and Effect** What are the causes and effects of increasing marginal returns?

3. **Draw Inferences** What steps can a business take to prevent marginal product of labor from decreasing?

Production Costs: Text

4. **Draw Conclusions** Read the section "Production Costs." What are the four types of costs that a business must consider in making business decisions?

5. **Analyze Visual Information** Use Figure 3.13 to explain why it is wiser for the beanbag company to produce 10 beanbags per hour rather than 11.

6. **Determine Meaning of Phrases** Explain the relationship between the terms *fixed cost, variable cost,* and *total cost.*

Setting Output: Text

7. **Draw Conclusions** Why would a business continue to produce additional units of an item after the marginal cost begins to rise?

8. **Identify Cause and Effect** Read the section "Responding to Price Changes." Explain the effect of a change in price of a good or service on a business's decision on output.

9. **Summarize** Read the section "The Shutdown Decision." When should a money-losing factory close?

Interactive Reading Notepad • Lesson 3.5

Lesson 3.6 Changes in Supply

Key Terms

subsidy   regulation

excise tax

Academic Vocabulary

Automation: the use of machines or equipment to perform tasks previously carried out by people

Controversial: subject to sharp disagreement

Compensate: to make up for

Lesson Objectives

1 **Explain** how factors such as input costs create change in supply.

2 **Identify** three ways that the government can influence the supply of goods.

3 **Identify** other non-price determinants that create changes in supply.

4 **Explain** how firms choose a location to produce goods.

Input Costs and Changes in Supply: Text

1. **Paraphrase** Read "The Effect of Input Costs on Supply." Explain how and why rising and falling input costs affect supply.

2. **Analyze Interactions** Give an example of changes in input costs that would cause a frozen yogurt company to reduce the supply of frozen yogurt it produced.

3. **Draw Inferences** After reading "The Effect of Technology on Input Costs," explain whether new technology always acts to lower input costs and thus increase supply. Why or why not?

Government Policies and Changes in Supply: Text

4. **Explain an Argument** The reading says that subsidies paid to farmers to take land out of cultivation penalize more efficient producers. Why is that the case?

5. **Determine Central Ideas** Look at the second paragraph in the section "Excise Taxes and Supply." What is the implication of the statement that "Excise taxes are indirect—they are built into the price of the good—so consumers may not realize that they are paying them"?

6. **Draw Inferences** If government regulation increases price and thus decreases supply, why does the government regulate any goods and services?

7. **Assess an Argument** Read the statement by former Secretary of the Treasury Henry Paulson about government regulation. Do you agree or disagree with Paulson? Explain your answer.

Other Non-Price Determinants That Create Changes in Supply: Text

8. **Identify Cause and Effect** Suppose the United States buys most of its bananas from one country. What would happen to the supply curve for bananas if that country experienced a drought? What could American food companies do to shift it in the opposite direction?

9. **Determine Central Ideas** Why do suppliers hold the goods they produce rather than selling them immediately if they expect higher prices in the future?

10. **Summarize** Complete this table based on what you have read in this lesson.

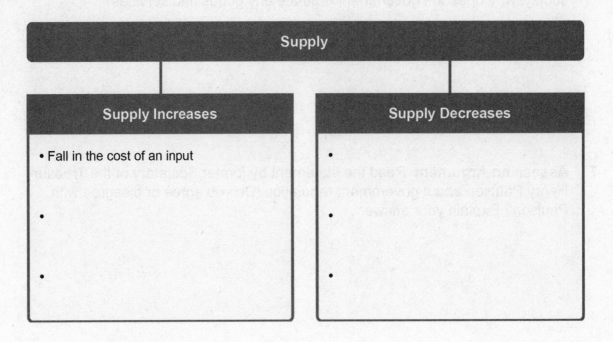

Supply	
Supply Increases	**Supply Decreases**
• Fall in the cost of an input • •	• • •

Deciding Where to Locate: Text

11. **Draw Conclusions** Why might an automaker want to have manufacturing plants in several different regions?

12. **Draw Conclusions** Why might a software company be less likely than the manufacturer of some larger, physical product to want facilities in several different regions?

Interactive Reading Notepad

Lesson 3.7 Equilibrium and Price Controls

Key Terms

equilibrium

disequilibrium

shortage

surplus

price ceiling

rent control

price floor

minimum wage

Academic Vocabulary

Stable: not changing or fluctuating

Flexible: capable of adjusting to new situations or conditions

---

Lesson Objectives

1 **Explain** how supply and demand create equilibrium in the marketplace.

2 **Describe** what happens to prices, quantities demanded, and quantities supplied when equilibrium is disturbed.

3 **Identify** two ways that the government intervenes in markets to control prices, including restricting the use of individual property.

4 **Analyze** the impacts of price ceilings and price floors on the free market.

Achieving Equilibrium: Text

1. **Identify Key Steps in a Process** You have been presented with two line graphs, exactly alike except for the position of the line on each graph. One graph is a demand curve, and the other a supply curve for the same product. How would you find the equilibrium price and quantity?

2. **Analyze Interactions** Read the section "Benefits to Buyers and Sellers." What is the advantage for consumers of buying goods at the equilibrium price? What is the advantage for producers of selling goods at the equilibrium price?

Effects of Disequilibrium: Text

3. **Determine Central Ideas** *Equilibrium* means "balance." What is out of balance when a market is in a state of disequilibrium?

4. **Identify Cause and Effect** Consider the market conditions that exist in the event of a shortage. Explain what role price is having on both buyers and sellers in this situation.

5. **Compare and Contrast** Examine Figure 3.18 and Figure 3.19. In what ways are these graphs similar? In what ways are they different?

Price Ceilings: Text

6. **Determine Central Ideas** Read the section "Effects of Government Rent Control." Does rent control result in a shortage or a surplus? Explain.

7. **Explain an Argument** In the section "Consequences of Ending Rent Control," you read that most economists argue that the benefits of ending rent control exceed the costs. Do you agree? Why or why not?

Price Floors: Text

8. **Explain an Argument** Read the section "The Minimum Wage." What are the basic economic arguments for and against a minimum wage?

9. **Compare and Contrast** Where on Figure 3.20 is the ceiling price in relation to the equilibrium price, and where on Figure 3.21 is the floor price in relation to the equilibrium price?

10. **Summarize** Complete the following concept web, based on the information in this lesson.

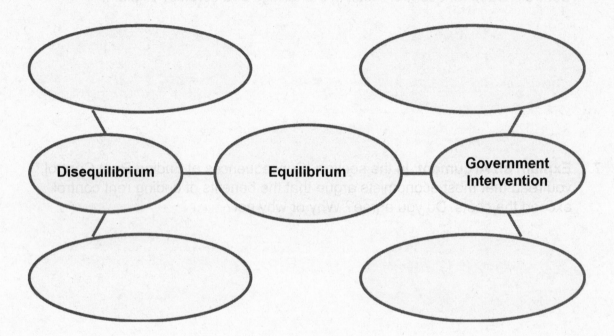

Interactive Reading Notepad • Lesson 3.7

Lesson 3.8 Changes in Market Equilibrium

Key Terms
inventory

search cost

Academic Vocabulary

Hypothetical: an imaginary example used to demonstrate a point

Trendy: newly fashionable

Lesson Objectives

1 **Explain** why a free market naturally tends to move toward equilibrium.

2 **Analyze** how a market reacts to an increase or decrease in supply.

3 **Analyze** how a market reacts to an increase or decrease in demand.

Tending Toward Equilibrium: Text

1. **Draw Conclusions** You see a poster in a store window that says, "Pre-Winter Sandal Blowout." Why do you think a store might offer a big discount on sandals in the fall?

2. **Identify Key Steps in a Process** What are the two factors that can push a market into disequilibrium?

Increasing Supply: Text

3. **Evaluate Explanations** Read the following explanation of what happens when the supply curve shifts to the right. What is wrong about this explanation?

   "The rightward shift of the supply curve unbalances market equilibrium and creates a temporary shortage. The shortage is eliminated by falling prices."

4. **Analyze Sequence** Consider the example of digital cameras discussed in this section. What development followed the development of new digital camera technology that lowered the cost of production for these devices?

5. **Analyze Sequence** What followed the event that you identified in your answer to Question 4?

Decreasing Supply: Text

6. **Draw Inferences** In the 1970s, the federal government imposed expensive antipollution regulations on auto producers. How would this have affected the supply curve for the automobile market? Why?

Increasing Demand: Text

7. **Compare and Contrast** Read the statement below. Do you agree or disagree with it? Explain.

"Search costs are like negative externalities. They are hidden costs that consumers must pay."

8. **Analyze Interactions** A new game has just come on the market with a huge advertising campaign, and people are lining up at stores to buy it. What is likely to happen, from an economics standpoint, and how are producers going to respond?

9. **Determine Central Ideas** Look at Figure 3.24. Does this graph represent an increase in demand or a decrease? How do you know?

Decreasing Demand: Text

10. **Determine Central Ideas** How do price and quantity return to their original equilibrium point after a fad has passed its peak of popularity?

11. **Summarize** Complete the following diagram, explaining how prices react in each situation.

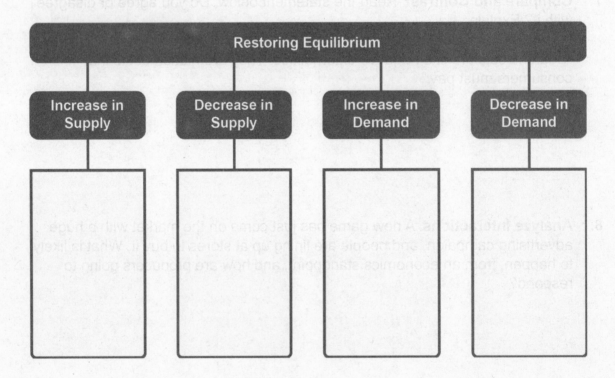

Restoring Equilibrium

| Increase in Supply | Decrease in Supply | Increase in Demand | Decrease in Demand |

Interactive Reading Notepad • Lesson 3.8

Lesson 3.9 Prices at Work

Key Terms

supply shock   black market

rationing   barter

Academic Vocabulary

Discount: a reduction in price used to attract buyers

Bureaucrat: an appointed official working in a government department

Diversity: variety

Lesson Objectives

1 **Identify** the many roles that prices play in a free enterprise system.

2 **List** the advantages of a price-based system.

3 **Examine** how a price-based system leads to a wider choice of goods and more efficient allocation of resources than systems such as barter or rationing.

4 **Describe** the relationship between prices and the profit incentive.

The Price System: Text

1. **Draw Inferences** Read the section "Prices in a Free Market." How does a free market economy differ from a centrally planned economy in the way each determines prices?

The Benefits of the Price System: Text

2. **Determine Central Ideas** How do you know, as a consumer shopping for a product, whether goods are in short supply or are readily available?

3. **Draw Inferences** If prices are like a traffic light, with green meaning demand is increasing and red meaning demand is decreasing, what might a yellow (caution) light signal to producers?

4. **Explain an Argument** Read the section "The Price System is 'Free.'" When economists argue that, unlike a command system, the price system is "free," what do they mean?

Choice and Efficiency: Text

5. **Summarize** Explain why the price system leads to greater choice for consumers than is available in centrally planned systems.

6. **Explain an Argument** Suppose that a recent hurricane in the Caribbean has caused a supply shock in the market for sugar in the United States. Think about the way that would affect the price of sugar. If you were an adviser to the President, which would you recommend—rationing sugar or taking no action? Explain your reasoning.

Prices and the Profit Incentive: Text

7. **Determine Central Ideas** Suppose you washed dishes at a restaurant, earning the minimum wage. What would motivate you to work the same number of hours, doing the same job, at a different restaurant?

8. **Identify Cause and Effect** Consider Adam Smith's example of the baker and the butcher. Why do you think bakers, butchers, and other producers tend to offer products that are favorites of their customers?

9. Draw Conclusions What is imperfect competition, and why is it a problem?

10. Summarize Complete the following concept web, based on the information in this lesson.

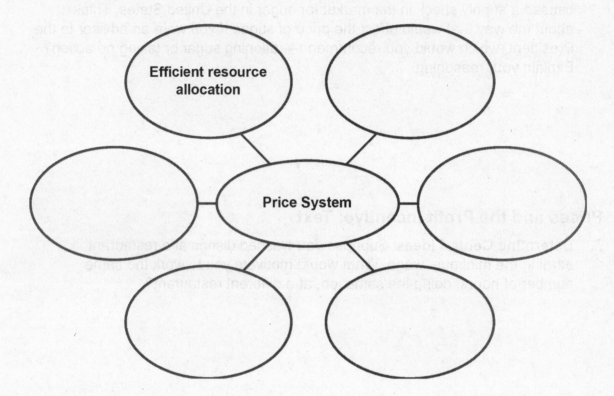

Interactive Reading Notepad • Lesson 3.9

Lesson 4.1 Pure Competition

Key Terms

pure competition

commodity

barriers to entry

imperfect competition

start-up costs

Academic Vocabulary

Element: factor; ingredient

Interact: work together; mutually influence

Intense: strong, deep

Available: on hand; able to be used

Lesson Objectives

1 **Describe** the characteristics and give examples of perfectly competitive markets.

2 **List** two common barriers that prevent firms from entering a market.

3 **Describe** prices and output in a perfectly competitive market.

Conditions for Pure Competition: Text

1. **Connect** How do incentives affect suppliers in a purely competitive market?

2. **Make Generalizations** The amount of a market that a producer controls is called market share. How is market share related to pure competition?

3. **Identify** What makes a product a commodity?

4. **Evaluate Explanations** Why would having information be a requirement for a purely competitive market?

5. **Connect** How is ease of market entry and exit related to the number of suppliers in a purely competitive market?

6. **Identify** Use the graphic organizer to label the missing conditions of pure competition and the characteristic that results from them.

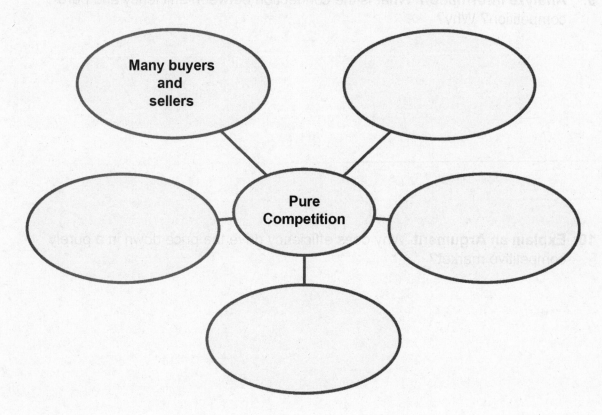

Barriers to Entry and Competition: Text

7. **Identify Cause and Effect** Why would high start-up costs serve as a barrier to competition?

8. **Identify Cause and Effect** Why is complex technology a barrier to competition?

Price, Output, and Purely Competitive Markets: Text

9. **Analyze Information** What is the connection between efficiency and pure competition? Why?

10. **Explain an Argument** Why does efficiency drive the price down in a purely competitive market?

Lesson 4.2 Monopolies

Key Terms

monopoly

economies of scale

natural monopoly

government monopoly

patent

franchise

license

price discrimination

market power

Academic Vocabulary

hydroelectric: generating electricity through the energy of running water

maximize: to increase or make the most of

exemption: freedom from an obligation, duty, or liability

Lesson Objectives

1 **Describe** the characteristics and give examples of a monopoly.

2 **Describe** how monopolies, including government monopolies, are formed.

3 **Explain** how a firm with a monopoly makes output decisions.

4 **Explain** why monopolists sometimes practice price discrimination.

Characteristics of a Monopoly: Text

1. **Categorize** As you read "Characteristics of a Monopoly," complete this graphic organizer.

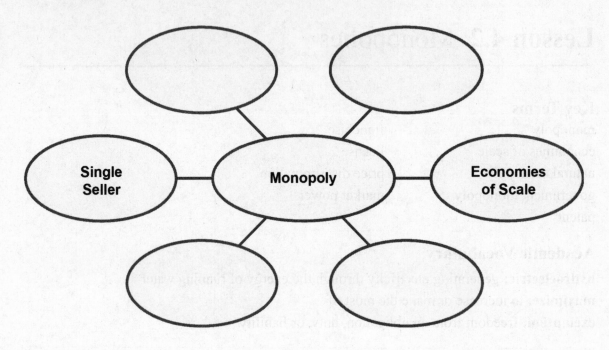

Single Seller — Monopoly — Economies of Scale

2. **Draw Conclusions** Why must a monopoly supply a good or service that has no close substitute?

3. **Cite Evidence** What would happen to a firm with limited economies of scale?

The Role of Government: Text

4. **Draw Inferences** Why do you think that patents expire after a set period of time?

5. **Categorize** Give three examples of a franchise.

Output Decisions: Text

6. **Cite Evidence** What happens when a monopolist lowers the price of a good?

7. **Identify Supporting Details** In a purely competitive market, what happens to price as output increases?

Price Discrimination: Text

8. **Categorize** Give three examples of price discrimination.

9. **Determine Central Ideas** What three conditions must a market meet in order for price discrimination to work?

Interactive Reading Notepad • Lesson 4.2

Lesson 4.3 Monopolistic Competition and Oligopoly

Key Terms

monopolistic competition   price war

differentiation   collusion

non-price competition   price fixing

oligopoly   cartel

Academic Vocabulary

Modified: changed or made less strong

Conventional: traditional

Tactic: a way of achieving a goal

Quota: a proportional share

Lesson Objectives

1 **Describe** characteristics and give examples of monopolistic competition.

2 **Explain** how firms compete without lowering prices.

3 **Understand** how firms in a monopolistically competitive market set output.

4 **Describe** characteristics and give examples of oligopoly.

Characteristics of Monopolistic Competition: Text

1. **Identify Supporting Details** What effect do barriers to entry have in a monopolistically competitive market?

2. **Draw Conclusions** How does differentiation help monopolistically competitive firms sell their products?

Non-price Competition: Text

3. **Classify** If your friend buys a brand of sneakers because his favorite basketball player wears them, what form of non-price competition is that?

4. **Support Ideas With Examples** Why is location a factor in non-price competition? Give an example in your answer.

Prices, Output, and Profits: Text

5. **Predict Consequences** If a monopolistically competitive brand-name product that you felt brand loyalty towards raised its price by a significant amount, what would you do? Explain your answer.

6. **Hypothesize** What might happen if price fixing were legal in the United States?

Characteristics of Oligopoly: Text

7. **Identify Cause and Effect** How do greater economies of scale lead to an oligopoly?

8. **Summarize** Why do cartels often not last very long?

Interactive Reading Notepad • Lesson 4.3

Lesson 4.4 Government Regulation and Competition

Key Terms

predatory pricing

merger

antitrust laws

deregulation

trust

Academic Vocabulary

Anticompetitive: likely to discourage competition

Predatory: inclined to mistreat others for profit

Appeal: request to have a legal case heard in a higher court

Enhance: increase; improve

Bankruptcy: the state of being legally bankrupt, or unable to pay off one's debts

---

Lesson Objectives

1 **Explain** why firms might try to increase their market power.

2 **List** three market practices that the government regulates or bans to protect competition.

3 **Define** *deregulation,* and list its effects on several industries.

Government and Competition: Text

1. **Analyze Word Choices** The words *predator* and *prey* often refer to animals. When you see the word *predatory,* what animal comes to mind? Who might be the prey in a predatory pricing scheme?

2. **Explain an Argument** Explain the government's argument that Microsoft engaged in anticompetitive practices.

3. **Draw Inferences** What economic benefits resulted from the breakup of AT&T?

4. **Analyze Interactions** Why do prices often rise after a merger or a series of mergers?

5. **Determine Central Ideas** Under what conditions will the government approve a merger?

Deregulation: Text

6. **Identify Cause and Effect** When the government deregulates an industry, what does it expect will happen?

7. **Draw Conclusions** How would you characterize the results of the deregulation of California's electricity market? Explain.

8. **Assess an Argument** Do you think the government had a good reason to question the merger of American Airlines and US Airways? Explain.

9. **Summarize** Complete the following chart, based on the information in this Lesson.

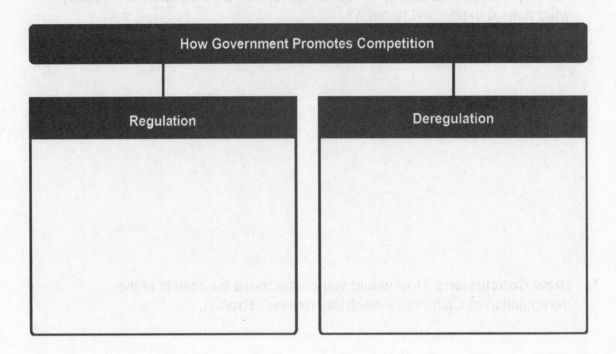

How Government Promotes Competition	
Regulation	Deregulation

Interactive Reading Notepad • Lesson 4.4

Lesson 5.1 Sole Proprietorships

Key Terms

sole proprietorship
business organization
business license

zoning laws
liability
fringe benefits

Academic Vocabulary

Entrepreneur: a person who decides how to combine resources to create goods and services

---

Lesson Objectives

1 **Explain** the characteristics of a sole proprietorship.

2 **Analyze** the advantages of a sole proprietorship.

3 **Analyze** the disadvantages of a sole proprietorship.

4 **Analyze** the economic rights and responsibilities involved in starting a small business.

The Role of Sole Proprietorships: Text

1. **Draw Inferences** Why do you think more than 70 percent of all businesses are organized as sole proprietorships?

2. **Compare and Contrast** How might someone with an entrepreneurial spirit be different from someone who has worked for a single company for many years?

3. **Use Visual Information** Look at the circle graph that shows characteristics of a sole proprietorship. What amount do most sole proprietors report on their taxes? What does this tell you about the size of most sole proprietorships?

Advantages of Sole Proprietorships: Text

4. **Assess an Argument** Maggie wants to name her artificial flower arrangement business using her name, "Maggie Lightner, Inc." Her friend Sally thinks she should name it "Forever Flower Designs." Think about the advantages of a sole proprietorship. Why might Maggie want to consider Sally's idea?

5. **Draw Conclusions** Why do you think zoning laws may prohibit some sole proprietors from operating businesses out of their homes?

6. **Assess an Argument** A sole proprietor has the ability to set flexible business hours. Why is this an advantage over other types of businesses?

Disadvantages of Sole Proprietorships: Text

7. **Categorize** Use the chart to classify advantages and disadvantages of sole proprietorships.

Advantages of Sole Proprietorships	Disadvantages of Sole Proprietorships

8. **Use Visual Information** Study the bar graph showing "Survival of Sole Proprietorships." Suppose there were 100 new sole proprietorships in Year 1. How many would still be in business in Year 3?

9. **Draw Inferences** A sole proprietor may have to turn down work if he or she does not have enough time to do it. The obvious cost of this is the loss of money the sole proprietor would have received for the work. What is a hidden cost of turning down work?

10. Identify Supporting Details Why might some sole proprietors have a difficult time taking vacation if they can set their hours to be whatever they want?

Lesson 5.2 Partnerships and Franchises

Key Terms

partnership

general partnership

limited partnership

limited liability partnership

articles of partnership

assets

business franchise

royalties

Academic Vocabulary

Complement: to balance, to provide a missing part or element that completes something

Professional: doctor, lawyer, accountant, or other person with an advanced degree

Register: to formally list one's name in an official record

Potential: having the possibility to cause or bring about some action or result

Benefit: to gain an advantage or positive outcome

Lesson Objectives

1 **Explain** the characteristics of different types of partnerships.

2 **Analyze** the advantages of partnerships.

3 **Analyze** the disadvantages of partnerships.

4 **Describe** how a business franchise operates.

The Characteristics of Partnerships: Text

1. **Determine Central Ideas** Based on the opening paragraphs of the section, what are the keys to determining if a partnership is appropriate?

2. Categorize What are the chief characteristics of a general partnership?

3. Analyze Interactions Think about how limited partners and general partners take part in business operations. How is the participation of limited partners different from the participation of general partners?

4. Compare and Contrast Use the graphic organizer to compare the characteristics of the three types of partnerships. For each type of partnership, identify each type of partner involved. Tell whether that partner's liability is limited or full. Then tell whether that partner's participation in the management of the business is limited or full.

Types of Partnerships		
	Liability	Business Management
General Partnership		
Limited Partnership		
Limited Liability Partnership		

Advantages of Partnerships: Text

5. **Summarize** What issues are addressed in the articles of a partnership?

6. **Evaluate Arguments** Suppose someone with whom you are about to enter a partnership says to you, "We don't need articles of partnership. We trust each other." What would you say?

7. **Draw Inferences** Why do you think people in partnerships find it easier to obtain loans than a person who operates a sole proprietorship?

Disadvantages of Partnerships: Text

8. **Categorize** Which disadvantage of partnerships is unique to one type? Which is shared by all types?

Interactive Reading Notepad • Lesson 5.2

9. **Solve Problems** What can two partners do to solve problems they are experiencing?

The Franchise Alternative: Text

10. **Summarize** What is the relationship between a franchiser and a franchisee?

11. **Compare and Contrast** How is owning a business franchise similar to being in a partnership? How is it different?

12. **Infer** Why do franchisers limit franchisees to a particular area?

13. Infer Use the graphic organizer to record the advantages and disadvantages of franchises.

Advantages of Franchises	Disadvantages of Franchises

Interactive Reading Notepad • Lesson 5.2

Lesson 5.3 Corporations

Key Terms

corporation	dividend
stock	limited liability corporation
closely held corporation	horizontal merger
publicly held corporation	vertical merger
bond	conglomerate
certificate of incorporation	multinational corporation

Academic Vocabulary

Liability: the legal obligation to pay debts

Crucial: extremely important

Regulate: to control according to law

Antitrust: opposing or intended to regulate business monopolies

Lesson Objectives

1 **Explain** the characteristics of corporations, including the creation of stocks and bonds.

2 **Analyze** the advantages of incorporation.

3 **Analyze** the disadvantages of incorporation.

4 **Compare and contrast** corporate combinations.

5 **Describe** the role of multinational corporations.

The Characteristics of Corporations: Text

1. **Identify Supporting Details** Explain how a closely held corporation differs from a publicly held corporation.

2. **Categorize** What role do corporate officers have in a corporation?

Advantages of Incorporation: Text

3. **Compare and Contrast** Describe the difference between stocks and bonds. Explain how each can benefit a corporation.

4. **Determine Central Ideas** Why can corporations exist longer than simple proprietorships or partnerships?

Disadvantages of Incorporation: Text

5. **Vocabulary: Use Context Clues** Why are dividends important to stockholders?

6. **Hypothesize** Given the fact that corporations often face double taxation, why do you think that business owners might still decide to incorporate?

Corporate Mergers: Text

7. **Identify Cause and Effect** Why is it that conglomerates don't tend to decrease competition?

8. **Draw Conclusions** In what instance would antitrust regulators become concerned about a vertical merger?

Multinational Corporations: Text

9. **Infer** Suppose a multinational corporation decides to open a new store or factory in another country. Use the graphic organizer to describe some advantages and disadvantages that a multinational corporation might pose for the country in which it opens the store or factory.

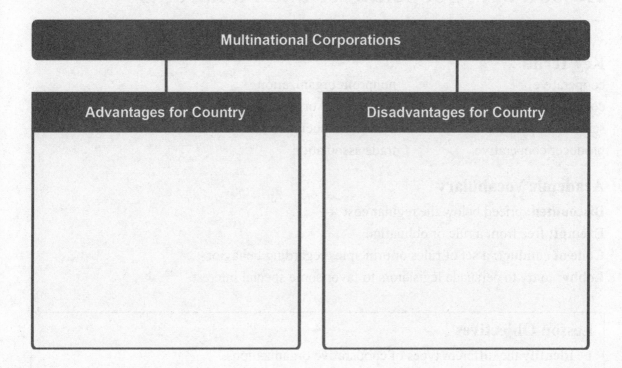

Interactive Reading Notepad • Lesson 5.3

Lesson 5.4 Cooperatives and Nonprofits

Key Terms

cooperative

consumer cooperative

service cooperative

producer cooperative

nonprofit organization

professional organization

business association

trade association

Academic Vocabulary

Discounted: priced below the regular cost

Exempt: free from a rule or obligation

Code of conduct: a set of rules or principles regarding behavior

Lobby: to try to persuade legislators to favor some special interest

---

Lesson Objectives

1 **Identify** the different types of cooperative organizations.

2 **Understand** the purpose of nonprofit organizations, including professional and business organizations.

Cooperatives: Text

1. **Determine Author's Purpose** Read the following quotation from Benjamin Franklin, taken from a newspaper, *The New-England Courant*, in 1722.

   "I would leave this to the Consideration of all who are concern'd for their own or their Neighbour's Temporal Happiness; and I am humbly of Opinion, that the Country is ripe for many such Friendly Societies, whereby every Man might help another, without any Disservice to himself."

Focus on this clause: "every Man might help another, without any Disservice to himself." How do these words describe what happens in a cooperative?

2. **Vocabulary: Determine Meaning** One of the principles of cooperatives is "voluntary and open membership." What do you think this means?

3. **Draw Conclusions** If you were a cotton farmer, why might you choose to join a cooperative? What type of cooperative would you join? Explain.

4. **Determine Central Ideas** Why can a credit union lend money to members at reduced rates?

5. **Generalize** Given that consumer cooperatives offer benefits to their members, what might be a reason that not everyone joins them?

Interactive Reading Notepad • Lesson 5.4

Nonprofits: Text

6. **Identify Supporting Beliefs** Why is the American Red Cross considered a nonprofit organization?

7. **Determine Central Ideas** How might a nonprofit professional organization help veterinarians?

8. **Draw Conclusions** Social networking Web sites have proven to be useful to nonprofits, especially charitable organizations and nongovernmental organizations. Why do you think this is so?

9. **Compare and Contrast** If you were a member of a city council, which type of nonprofit would you most likely deal with regularly—a business association or a professional association? Explain.

Interactive Reading Notepad • Lesson 5.4

Lesson 5.5 The Labor Force

Key Terms

labor force
outsourcing
offshoring
learning effect

screening effect
contingent employment
guest workers

Academic Vocabulary

Deregulation: the removal of regulations and restrictions

Trend: general direction in which something is changing

Released: let go after being employed

Lesson Objectives

1 **Describe** how trends in the labor force are tracked.

2 **Analyze** past and present occupational trends.

3 **Summarize** how the U.S. labor force is changing.

4 **Explain** trends in the wages and benefits paid to U.S. workers.

Tracking the Labor Force: Text

1. **Compare and Contrast** According to the lesson, the U.S. economy has, over the past two decades, shifted from a manufacturing economy toward a service-producing economy. How do economists differentiate between the two?

2. **Draw Inferences** What do you think the fact that the U.S. economy has shifted to a service-producing economy might mean for you as you begin a job search? What jobs are more likely to be available to you? What jobs are less likely to be available?

Occupational Trends: Text

3. **Vocabulary: Use Context Clues** Read the section titled "A Changing Economy." Why do you think the term *energized* is used to describe the changing economy of the mid-to-late 1800s?

4. **Draw Inferences** What improvements to computers do you think make it possible for them to be used in fields such as agriculture and forestry?

5. **Draw Inferences** Why do you think our nation has become a service economy? Do you think there is any relationship between the shift from manufacturing industries to service industries and the fact that jobs being shipped overseas? If so, what is that relationship?

6. **Summarize** What are some effects that outsourcing and offshoring have had on the U.S. economy?

The Changing Labor Force: Text

7. **Draw Inferences** There are benefits to having only permanent employees at a company, and there are benefits to replacing such employees with temporary workers. Which do you think is better for a company. Why?

8. **Analyze Interactions** Why do you think the number of women in the labor force has nearly doubled in the last 50 years?

Wages and Benefits Trends: Text

9. **Summarize** Why have real average wages decreased in the last couple of decades?

10. **Vocabulary: Use Context Clues** According to the Lesson, benefits are an important part of the compensation given to workers for their labor. Give examples of these benefits, and explain why you think they are so important to employees.

Lesson 5.6 Labor and Wages

Key Terms

derived demand	skilled labor
productivity of labor	professional labor
equilibrium wage	glass ceiling
unskilled labor	labor union
semi-skilled labor	featherbedding

Academic Vocabulary

Equilibrium: a state of balance

Lesson Objectives

1 **Analyze** how supply and demand in the labor market affect wage levels.

2 **Describe** how skill levels and education affect wages.

3 **Explain** how laws against wage discrimination affect wage levels.

4 **Identify** other factors affecting wage levels, such as minimum wage and workplace safety laws.

Supply, Demand, and the Labor Force: Text

1. **Identify Cause and Effect** What drives the demand for workers in the auto industry? Explain.

2. **Use Visual Information** Look at the Labor Demand graph. Why is the labor demand curve negatively sloped?

3. **Assess an Argument** Jonah is looking for a summer job. He decides that working for the city as a trash collector is likely to pay more money than working at the ice cream shop. Explain why his argument makes sense.

Labor and Skills: Text

4. **Compare and Contrast** Choose a job that requires unskilled labor and a job that requires professional labor. Compare and contrast the two jobs. What are the advantages and disadvantages of each?

5. **Draw Conclusions** Why is the supply of professional labor generally lower than the supply of unskilled or semi-skilled labor?

Discrimination in the Labor Market: Text

6. **Determine Central Ideas** Describe a situation in which a worker might decide to take legal action against his or her employer.

7. **Vocabulary: Use Context Clues** Look at how the term *human capital* is used in the section on wage discrimination. Based on the text, how would you define *human capital*?

8. **Paraphrase** As far as wages are concerned, what is the purpose of the anti-discrimination laws described in the reading?

Additional Factors Affecting Wages: Reading

9. **Determine Central Ideas** Complete the concept map to show factors that affect wages.

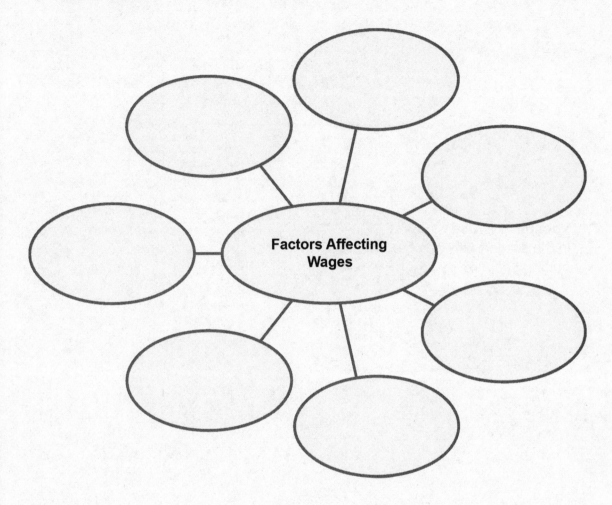

10. **Draw Inferences** How can hiring temporary workers reduce the labor costs of a company?

Interactive Reading Notepad • Lesson 5.6

11. Explain an Argument Use a real-world example to explain the argument by economists that unions depress the wages of all workers.

Lesson 5.7 Labor Unions

Key Terms

strike

right-to-work law

blue-collar worker

white-collar worker

collective bargaining

mediation

arbitration

Academic Vocabulary

mandatory: required

Lesson Objectives

1 **Explain** why American workers have formed labor unions.

2 **Summarize** the history of the labor movement in the United States.

3 **Analyze** the reasons for the decline of the labor movement.

4 **Explain** how labor and management negotiate contracts.

Organized Labor: Text

1. **Identify Cause and Effect** Suppose there are not many workers who can perform a particular job which is in high demand. What effect would the short supply of workers have on wages offered to workers to perform this job?

2. **Identify Supporting Details** What are two factors that have caused labor union membership to decline significantly over the past 50 years?

The History of the Labor Movement: Text

3. **Draw Conclusions** Why do you think factory owners forced workers to toil in such poor conditions for low wages in the 1800s?

4. **Draw Inferences** Why do you think that courts regarded unions as illegal in the earliest years of the labor movement?

5. **Draw Inferences** What do you think would have happened if unions hadn't formed?

The Decline in Labor Union Membership: Text

6. **Hypothesize** The text says that some unions preserved outdated and inefficient production methods to protect jobs. How might this have hurt the labor movement in the long run?

7. **Use Context Clues** Why do you think measures that ban mandatory union membership are called right-to-work laws?

8. **Summarize** Summarize the structural changes in the U.S. economy that have caused union membership to decline.

Labor and Management: Text

9. **Identify Key Steps in a Process** What are some steps that might be involved in the process used by unions and management to negotiate a contract?

10. **Draw Inferences** Why does a strike have the potential to seriously damage a company?

11. **Identify Cause and Effect** The number of work stoppages in the United States has declined over time. What are some factors that may have caused the drop in the number of work stoppages?

12. **Identify Supporting Details** Use the graphic organizer to explain how labor unions support the interests of workers. Name features of a union contract that promote these interests, and describe the tools that labor unions use to promote these interests.

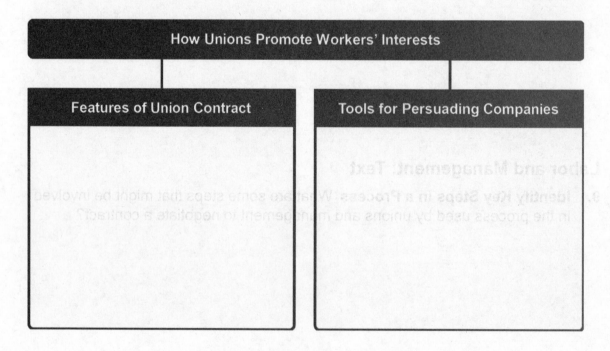

How Unions Promote Workers' Interests

Features of Union Contract

Tools for Persuading Companies

Lesson 6.1 The Role of Money

Key Terms

money

medium of exchange

barter

unit of account

store of value

currency

commodity money

representative money

specie

fiat money

Academic Vocabulary

Characteristic: quality or trait

Function: use, purpose

Transaction: an exchange, purchase, or transfer of goods or services

Circulation: the act of passing something among people in a large group

Lesson Objectives

1 **Describe** the uses and functions of money.

2 **List** the characteristics of money, including its commodity and representative forms.

3 **Analyze** the positive and negative aspects of currency, as well as other media of exchange.

The Three Uses of Money: Text

1. **Categorize** Name and give examples of two of the three functions of money. (Do not cite examples provided in the Lesson.)

2. **Define** In your own words, how would you define *money*?

The Six Characteristics of Money: Text

3. **Draw Conclusions** Explain why cattle would not be good to use as money today.

4. **Draw Inferences** One of the characteristics of money is that it is durable. Why is it important that money be durable?

5. **Summarize** How has currency changed over time?

Sources of Money's Value: Text

6. Summarize How does commodity money differ from fiat money?

7. Analyze Interactions Describe how money's portability, uniformity, and divisibility have impacted recent purchases you have made.

8. Draw Inferences Unlike a cow or tobacco, bills and coins have little or no real value in and of themselves. So, what do you think makes bills and coins valuable?

Lesson 6.2 Changes in American Banking

Key Terms

bank

national bank

bank runs

greenbacks

gold standard

central bank

Federal Reserve Banks

member banks

Federal Reserve Board

short-term loans

Federal Reserve Notes

foreclosures

Academic Vocabulary

Entrust: to put trust in

Regulations: rules and restrictions

Decentralized: dispersed from a central location

Creditworthy: having a satisfactory credit rating

Fraud: deceit, trickery, or breach of confidence

Lesson Objectives

1 **Describe** the shifts between centralized and decentralized banking in the United States before the Civil War.

2 **Explain** how government reforms stabilized the banking system in the later 1800s.

3 **Describe** changes in banking in the early 1900s, including the abandonment of the gold standard.

4 **Explain** the causes of two recent banking crises.

American Banking Before the Civil War: Text

1. Summarize In the debate over banking after the American Revolution, what did the Federalists advocate?

2. Assess an Argument According to the Lesson, the Federalists and the Antifederalists disagreed in principle about the role the national government should take in banking. Do you think one side had a more valid argument? Why or why not?

3. Draw Inferences Why was the period between 1837 and 1863 known as the Free Banking or "Wildcat" Era?

Stability in the Later 1800s: Text

4. Vocabulary: Use Context Clues Read the second paragraph of "Currencies of the Civil War." What do you think *backed* means?

5. **Draw Inferences** What benefits did the gold standard provide the nation?

Banking in the Early 1900s: Text

6. **Summarize** How did the Federal Reserve help to stabilize the economic and banking systems in the United States?

7. **Analyze Interactions Among Events** Why was the federal banking system created by the Federal Reserve Act of 1913 unable to prevent the Great Depression?

Two Crises for Banking: Text

8. **Compare and Contrast** How did the savings and loan crises of the 1970s and 1980s compare to earlier crises such as those of the Free Banking or "Wildcat" Era or the events leading up to the Great Depression?

9. **Vocabulary: Use Context Clues** According to the Lesson, a financial "meltdown" began in 2006. What do you think is meant by *meltdown*?

10. **Analyze Interactions Among Events** How did deregulation, directly or indirectly, contribute to the Savings and Loan Crises of the 1970s and 1980s?

Lesson 6.3 The Federal Reserve System

Key Terms

monetary policy

reserves

reserve requirements

check clearing

bank holding company

federal funds rate

discount rate

Academic Vocabulary

Prominent: important, significant

Charter: a legal document that specifies the organization, functions, and authority of an institution

Academic: related to higher education, especially colleges and universities

Agent: an individual or organization that has the legal authority to act on behalf of another

Stability: a condition in which the economy proceeds without wide fluctuations

---

Lesson Objectives

1 **Describe** banking history in the United States.

2 **Explain** the structure of the Federal Reserve System.

3 **Explain** how the Federal Reserve System policies affect the money supply and the broader economy.

4 **Analyze** the basic tools used by the Federal Reserve System to carry out United States monetary policy.

A Review of U.S. Banking History: Text

1. **Paraphrase** What do central banks do?

2. **Draw Inferences** Review the history of the First and Second Banks of the United States in the reading. What can you conclude about the effectiveness of the two banks?

3. **Draw Conclusions** Review the explanation of banking reserves in the Lesson. How does a bank benefit from having low reserves? What risk does it run if it has low reserves?

4. **Summarize** What two problems was Congress trying to solve in creating the Federal Reserve System?

The History of the Federal Reserve System: Text

5. **Summarize** Use the diagram below to identify key events in the history of the Federal Reserve System.

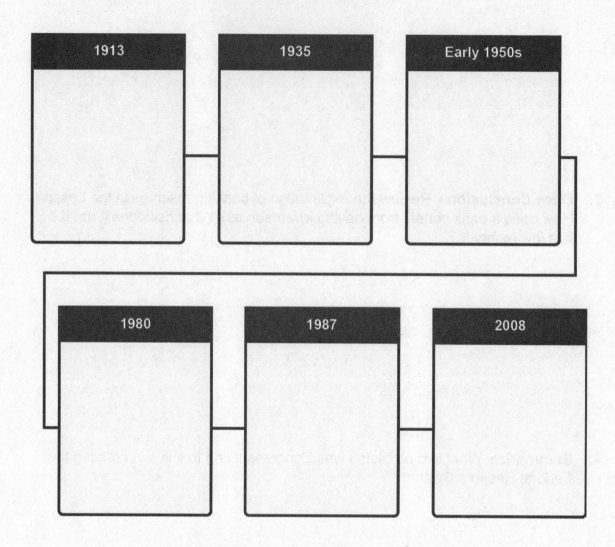

6. **Determine Author's Purpose** Read the passage from the Federal Reserve Board, about the situation in the small Minnesota town in the 1930s. What is the author's purpose in writing this passage?

7. **Cite Evidence** State three features of the structure and composition of the Federal Reserve System that contribute to its independence from the government.

8. **Draw Inferences** Why do banks become members of the Federal Reserve System?

The Structure of the Federal Reserve System: Text

9. **Summarize** What is the key function of the Federal Open Market Committee (FOMC)?

The Fed's Roles: Serving the Government: Text

10. **Determine Central Ideas** What is the relationship between the Fed and the Treasury?

11. **Draw Inferences** Where do the income tax payments that the Treasury receives go?

The Fed's Roles: Serving and Regulating Banks: Text

12. **Determine Central Ideas** What does the phrase "lender of last resort" mean?

13. **Cite Evidence** What unusual steps did the Fed take in the 2008 financial crisis? What can you conclude about that financial crisis, compared to earlier difficult economic times, from these actions?

14. **Draw Inferences** The Lesson says that each bank must report its reserves every day to the Fed, allowing it to monitor the money supply. What other purpose does this reporting serve?

15. **Draw Inferences** What kind of information do you think a member bank would need to provide to a District Bank examiner?

The Fed's Roles: Regulating the Money Supply: Text

16. **Summarize** How do higher interest rates affect people's decisions to save or spend their money?

17. **Integrate Information From Diverse Sources** Which part of the Federal Reserve System regulates the money supply?

Interactive Reading Notepad • Lesson 6.3

Lesson 6.4 The Functions of Modern Banks

Key Terms

money supply

liquidity

demand deposits

money market mutual funds

fractional reserve banking

default

mortgage

credit card

interest

principal

Academic Vocabulary

Obligated: required

Debt: the amount of money owed

Regulate: to oversee by law

Lesson Objectives

1 **Identify** different types of financial institutions and the services they provide.

2 **Explain** the benefits provided by financial institutions in the context of our free enterprise system.

3 **Describe** the development of electronic banking.

The Money Supply: Text

1. **Draw Inferences** What is an example of a situation in which a person would transfer money from an M2 account to an M1 account?

2. **Draw Conclusions** Why would a person want assets with liquidity?

3. **Contrast** What is the main difference between M1 and M2?

Functions of Financial Institutions: Text

4. **Summarize** Why do people use banks?

5. **Identify Cause and Effect** What might cause a person or business to default on a loan?

6. **Determine Meaning of Words** Read the last paragraph of "Mortgages." What do you think the term *fixed-rate mortgage* means? There are also loans known as *adjustable-rate mortgages*. What do you think those are?

7. **Identify Supporting Details** What reasons might a bank give for deciding that a loan applicant is not creditworthy?

Types of Financial Institutions: Text

8. **Draw Conclusions** Why might someone choose to save her money in a credit union rather than a commercial bank?

9. **Draw Inferences** Why do you think credit unions have that name?

Budgeting: Text

10. Analyze Interactions Why would a person decide to purchase a good with a debit card instead of a credit card?

11. Categorize What are some examples of stored-value cards?

12. Draw Inferences Why would a person choose to conduct home banking?

Interactive Reading Notepad • Lesson 6.4

Lesson 6.5 Investing

Key Terms

investment

financial system

financial asset

financial intermediary

mutual fund

hedge fund

diversification

portfolio

prospectus

return

Academic Vocabulary

Expansion: an increase in the size, volume, or scope of something

Essence: the intrinsic properties that characterize or identify something

Intermediary: acting as an agent between persons or things

Lesson Objectives

1 **Describe** how investing contributes to the free enterprise system.

2 **Explain** how investing brings together savers and borrowers in the free enterprise system.

3 **Explain** how different types of financial institutions serve as intermediaries between savers and borrowers.

4 **Analyze** liquidity, return, and risk within the free enterprise system.

Investment and Free Enterprise: Text

1. **Summarize** How does our free enterprise system promote economic growth through investing?

The Financial System: Text

2. **Identify Key Steps in a Process** As you read "The Financial System," use this graphic organizer to identify the process by savers lend money to people who need it.

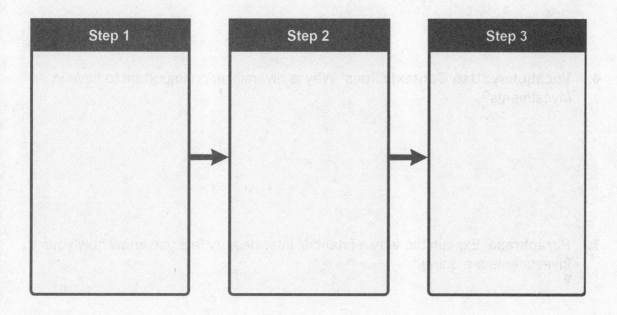

Step 1 → Step 2 → Step 3

3. **Identify Supporting Details** Why do savers need documentation such as monthly statements or bond certificates?

Financial Intermediaries: Text

4. **Identify Supporting Details** Why do people invest in mutual funds rather than in single stocks?

5. **Compare and Contrast** What is the difference between life insurance and a pension?

6. **Vocabulary: Use Context Clues** Why is diversification important to have in investments?

7. **Paraphrase** Explain the way a financial intermediary lets you know how your investments are doing.

Liquidity, Return, and Risk: Text

8. **Draw Conclusions** What are the benefits of bank savings accounts and CDs, and why might you choose one over the other?

9. **Draw Inferences** Would it be better to lend your money to a bank at a 2 percent interest rate or to a friend at a 4 percent interest rate? Explain your answer.

Lesson 6.6 Bonds and Other Financial Assets

Key Terms

coupon rate

maturity

par value

yield

savings bond

inflation-indexed bond

municipal bond

corporate bond

junk bond

capital market

money market

primary market

secondary market

Academic Vocabulary

Finance: to pay for

Enterprise: a venture

Security: an asset that can be traded

Indenture agreement: a contract that lists the payment terms of a loan

Expenditure: expense

Lesson Objectives

1 **Describe** the characteristics of bonds as financial assets.

2 **Explain** how corporations raise money through bonds.

3 **Describe** the characteristics of other types of financial assets.

4 **List** four different types of financial asset markets.

Bonds as Financial Assets: Text

1. **Identify Cause and Effect** What would cause a bondholder to sell a bond before it reaches maturity?

2. **Summarize** Why would an investor purchase a bond?

3. **Identify Supporting Details** Issuing a bond poses both advantages and disadvantages. Use the graphic organizer to list them.

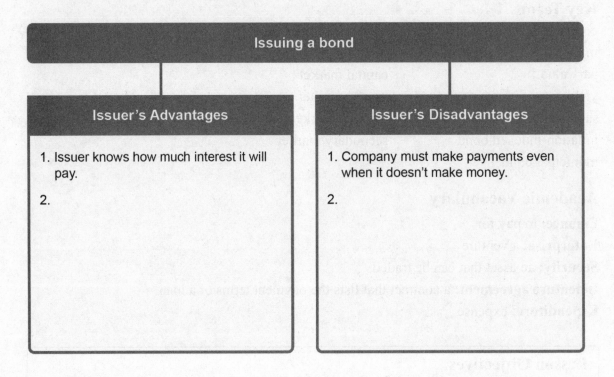

Issuing a bond	
Issuer's Advantages	**Issuer's Disadvantages**
1. Issuer knows how much interest it will pay. 2.	1. Company must make payments even when it doesn't make money. 2.

Types of Bonds: Text

4. **Draw Inferences** Why do you think government bonds usually have a low risk of default?

5. **Apply Concepts** If a business wanted to construct a new office building, replace all its equipment, and hire new employees, what type of bond would it issue?

6. **Determine Meaning of Words** Read the last paragraph of "Junk Bonds." What do you think the word *speculative* means?

Other Types of Financial Assets: Text

7. **Draw Inferences** What is a disadvantage of buying a certificate of deposit (CD)?

8. **Determine Central Ideas** What are the benefits of investing in a money market mutual fund?

Financial Asset Markets: Text

9. **Categorize** Long-term CDs and corporate and government bonds that require more than a year to mature are examples of what kind of market?

10. **Categorize** Assets that can be resold to other buyers are on what kind of market?

Lesson 6.7 Stocks

Key Terms

share

capital gain

capital loss

stock split

stockbroker

brokerage firm

stock exchange

futures

options

call option

put option

bull market

bear market

speculation

Academic Vocabulary

Bankruptcy: the state of being legally declared bankrupt, or unable to pay off one's debts

Contract: a formal, legally binding agreement

Circulation: the flow of something among people in a group

Stimulate: to encourage the development of something

Lesson Objectives

1 **Describe** how stocks are traded.

2 **Describe** the benefits and risks of buying stock.

3 **Explain** how corporations raise money through stocks and bonds.

4 **Explain** how stock performance is measured.

5 **Assess** the ways to be a wise investor in the stock market.

Investing in Stock: Text

1. **Draw Conclusions** Why might someone choose to invest in income stocks rather than growth stocks?

2. **Compare and Contrast** What are the two main ways that corporations can raise money from investors? How do those two methods affect investors differently?

3. **Draw Conclusions** Why might a person sell a stock even though it would leave them with a capital loss?

4. **Explain an Argument** Do you think the benefits of investing in stock outweigh the risks? Why or why not?

Stock Trading: Text

5. **Assess an Argument** Suppose you ask an older relative for advice on your first purchase of stock, and she says, "Avoid brokerage firms. Just get yourself some trading software and save having to pay a commission." Is this sound advice? Why or why not?

6. **Compare and Contrast** If you wanted to buy shares of a corporation that makes computer chips, which stock exchange would you more likely use, the New York Stock Exchange or Nasdaq? Why?

7. **Determine Central Ideas** An online list of futures prices could tell an investor how much a commodity is likely to cost six months or nine months from now. Do you agree or disagree? Explain.

Tracking Stock Performance: Text

8. **Draw Inferences** Is it always smart to buy stock during a bull market? Why or why not?

9. **Cite Evidence** The Dow Jones Industrial Average reflects the average value of a set of just 30 stocks. Why do so many people rely on the Dow as an indicator of how the stock market is doing?

The Great Crash and Beyond: Text

10. **Draw Inferences** During the 1920s, many Americans bought appliances and other expensive goods on credit. What does that say about their attitude concerning the state of the economy?

11. **Determine Author's Point of View** Do you think the following poem was written before or after the Great Crash? Explain the author's intent.

> Oh, hush thee, my babe, granny's bought some shares
> Daddy's gone out to play with the bulls and the bears
> Mother's buying on tips, and she simply can't lose
> And Baby shall have some expensive new shoes
> —Appeared in *The Saturday Evening Post*, 1929

12. **Identify Cause and Effect** Why did Americans avoid investing in the stock market from the 1940s to the 1980s?

13. **Assess an Argument** Some analysts contend that fear and uncertainty undermine the stock market. How do events from the early 2000s support that argument?

Lesson 7.1 Gross Domestic Product

Key Terms

national income accounting

gross domestic product

intermediate goods

durable goods

nondurable goods

nominal GDP

real GDP

gross national product

depreciation

price level

aggregate supply

aggregate demand

Academic Vocabulary

Externality: an economic side effect of a good or service that generates benefits or costs to someone other than the person deciding how much to produce or consume

Discrepancy: a conflict or variation between facts, figures, and claims

---

Lesson Objectives

1 **Explain** how gross domestic product (GDP) is calculated.

2 **Interpret** GDP data.

3 **Identify** factors that influence GDP.

4 **Describe** other output and income measures.

Economic Measures: Text

1. **Cite Evidence** Explain how buying a shirt contributes to the GDP. Relate it to all four parts of the definition of GDP: *dollar value*, *final goods and services*, *produced within a country's borders*, and *in a given year*.

2. **Compare and Contrast** How is the expenditure approach different from the income approach to calculating GDP?

3. **Categorize** Categorize each of the following as a durable good or a nondurable good: a car, a microwave oven, a can of tomato sauce, a pair of pants, a cleaning product, a ceiling fan.

Two Measures of GDP: Text

4. **Analyze Interactions** Suppose the nominal GDP for year A is $500,000 and the nominal GDP for the same economy in year B is $400,000. The real GDP for year A is $500,000, and the real GDP for year B is $500,000. The same amount of goods and services were produced each year. What happened to the prices of goods and services between year A and year B? Explain.

What GDP Doesn't Measure: Text

5. **Determine Central Ideas** Before you read "What GDP Doesn't Measure," complete the "About GDP" section of the graphic organizer. As you read "What GDP Doesn't Measure," complete the "Drawbacks to GDP" section of the graphic organizer.

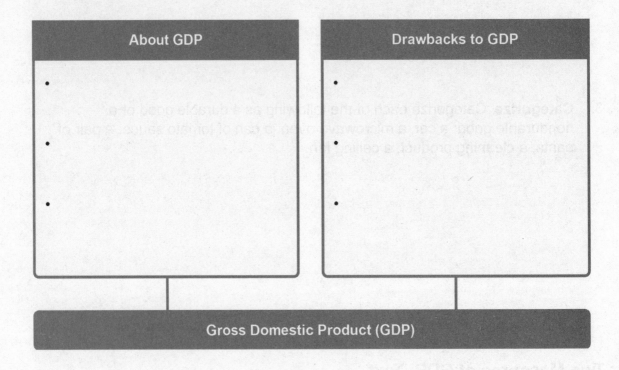

About GDP	Drawbacks to GDP
•	•
•	•
•	•

Gross Domestic Product (GDP)

6. **Summarize** Give an example of each of the following limitations of GDP: nonmarket activities, the underground economy, negative externalities, and quality of life.

Other Economic Measures: Text

7. **Analyze Interactions** How is gross national product related to gross domestic product?

8. **Draw Conclusions** One of the measures derived from GDP is personal income. If personal income is on the rise, how would you expect the GDP to reflect this?

Factors that Affect GDP: Text

9. **Identify Cause and Effect** How does the aggregate supply change as GDP rises? How does aggregate demand change as GDP rises?

10. **Use Visual Information** Refer to the Equilibrium Aggregate Supply and Demand Graph. How will a shift to the right in an AD curve affect the equilibrium GDP and the equilibrium price level?

Lesson 7.2 Business Cycles

Key Terms

business cycle	recession
expansion	depression
economic growth	stagflation
peak	business investment
contraction	leading indicators
trough	

Academic Vocabulary

Macroeconomic: dealing with the broad and general aspects of an economy

Fluctuation: continual change from one point or condition to another

Unemployment rate: the percentage of workers who want to be employed but are not

Downturn: a turn or trend downward

Aggregate: a sum, total, or combined amount

Demand: the desire to purchase combined with the power to do so

Output: the quantity or amount produced in a given time

Expectations: the act or state of expecting

Consumer confidence: a measure of how consumers feel about the economy

Ripple effect: a series of consequences caused by a single action or event

Forecasters: those who predict a future condition or consequence

Capitalism: private ownership of the means of production, distribution, and exchange

Consumer spending: the amount spent by consumers in an economy

---

Lesson Objectives

1 **Analyze** business cycles using economic data.

2 **Describe** four factors that keep business cycles going.

3 **Explain** how economists predict changes in business cycles.

4 **Analyze** the impact of business cycles in U.S. history.

Business Cycle Phases: Text

1. **Draw Inferences** Why do you think economists can be certain that every expansion in the economy will be followed by a peak and then a contraction?

2. **Compare and Contrast** According to the Lesson, a recession and a depression are not the same thing. How do economists differentiate between the two?

What Drives Business Cycles?: Text

3. **Vocabulary: Use Context Clues** Read the section titled "Effects of External Shocks." Why do you think the term *external* is used to describe these shocks to the economy?

4. **Draw Inferences** Why do you think rising interest rates affect purchases of "big ticket" items more than other purchases?

5. **Summarize** What role do consumer expectations play in the economy? How can they affect business cycles?

Forecasting Business Cycles: Text

6. **Summarize** Give an example of a leading indicator, and explain how using this can help economists to predict future trends in a business cycle.

7. **Analyze Interactions** Why do you think John J. Raskob, Senior Financial Officer for General Motors, was so far off in his prediction in the summer of 1929?

Business Cycles in the United States: Text

8. **Compare and Contrast** How did the Great Depression of the 1930s compare to the economic recession that began in 2008?

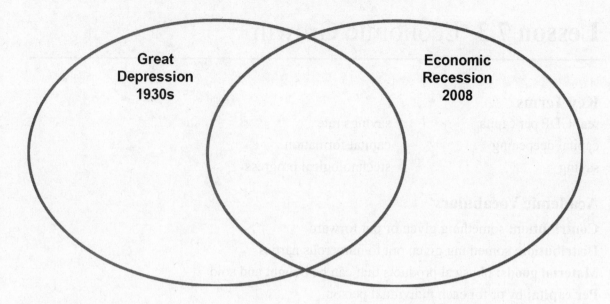

Great
Depression
1930s

Economic
Recession
2008

9. **Vocabulary: Use Context Clues** According to the Lesson, the recession of the 1970s and 1980s began when an international cartel, OPEC, placed an embargo on oil shipped to the United States. What do you think is meant by *embargo*?

Interactive Reading Notepad • Lesson 7.2

Lesson 7.3 Economic Growth

Key Terms

real GDP per capita

capital deepening

saving

savings rate

capital formation

stechnological progress

Academic Vocabulary

Contribution: something given or put forward

Distribution: something given out to numerous parties

Material goods: physical products that can be bought and sold

Per capita: by or for each individual person

Lesson Objectives

1 **Analyze** how economic growth is measured.

2 **Analyze** how productivity, technology, and trade relate to economic growth.

3 **Summarize** the impact of population growth and government policies on economic growth.

4 **Analyze** how saving and investment are related to economic growth.

5 **Explain** how the functions of financial institutions affect households and businesses.

Measuring Economic Growth: Text

1. **Determine Meaning of Words** Read the section "Measuring Economic Growth." Explain in your own words what "real GDP per capita" means. Why do we need the "per capita" part to measure growth?

2. **Determine Central Ideas** Does a rising GDP benefit everyone? Explain.

Capital Deepening: Text

3. **Identify Cause and Effect** As you read the section on capital deepening, use this graphic organizer to record the causes of capital deepening and its effects.

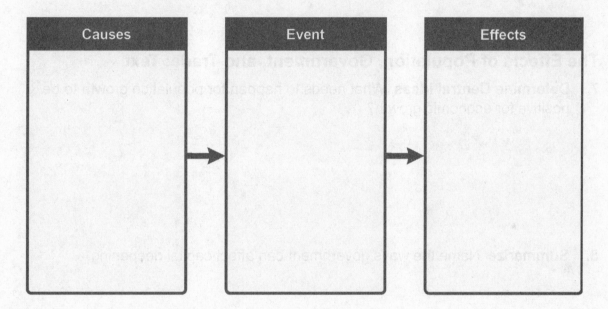

4. **Paraphrase** What can an individual do to affect capital deepening?

Saving and Investment: Text

5. **Summarize** Why is the savings rate important for capital deepening?

6. **Determine Central Ideas** How are savings and investment related?

The Effects of Population, Government, and Trade: Text

7. **Determine Central Ideas** What needs to happen for population growth to be positive for economic growth?

8. **Summarize** Name the ways government can affect capital deepening.

9. **Analyze Interactions** Explain the conditions under which trade deficits spur capital deepening and conditions when they fail to do so.

Technological Progress: Text

10. Explain an Argument How does technological progress affect productivity?

11. Analyze Sequence What are three factors that contribute to economic growth? List them in order of size from smallest to largest.

12. Summarize What are the causes of technological progress?

Lesson 7.4 Unemployment

Key Terms

frictional unemployment
structural unemployment
globalization
seasonal unemployment
cyclical unemployment

unemployment rate
full employment
underemployed
discouraged worker

Academic Vocabulary

Recession: a long decline in business activity

Policymaker: someone who plans actions for government, political parties, or business

Discouraged: having lost confidence or hope

Lesson Objectives

1 **Interpret** economic data relating to the unemployment rate.

2 **Differentiate** between frictional, seasonal, structural, and cyclical unemployment.

3 **Explain** why full employment does not mean that every worker is employed.

4 **Explain** the costs and benefits of U.S. economic policies related to the goal of full employment.

Types of Unemployment: Text

1. **Categorize** As you read "Types of Unemployment," use this graphic organizer to categorize the four different types of unemployment.

Frictional Unemployment	Structural Unemployment	Seasonal Unemployment	Cyclical Unemployment

2. **Summarize** Explain the economic policy that was passed after the cyclical unemployment of the Great Depression.

The Unemployment Rate: Text

3. **Identify Key Steps in a Process** Use the BLS measure of determining the unemployment rate. If a nation has 120 million employed people and 15 million unemployed people, what is the unemployment rate?

4. **Paraphrase** Explain why the unemployment rate is seasonally adjusted.

The Goal of Full Employment: Text

5. **Draw Conclusions** Why does an economy that has full employment have frictional, seasonal, and structural unemployment but not cyclical unemployment?

6. **Identify Supporting Details** In the reading, why was Jim the philosophy major an example of someone who is underemployed?

Lesson 7.5 Inflation and Deflation

Key Terms

inflation

purchasing power

price index

Consumer Price Index

market basket

inflation rate

core inflation rate

hyperinflation

quantity theory

wage-price spiral

fixed income

deflation

Academic Vocabulary

Expenditure: an act of spending; an amount spent

Lesson Objectives

1 **Interpret** data that reflect the rate of inflation.

2 **Explain** the effects of rising prices.

3 **Identify** the causes of inflation.

4 **Describe** recent trends in the rate of inflation.

How Rising Prices Affect You: Text

1. **Assess an Argument** The Barrows decide not to sell their house even though it is worth ten times more than what they paid for it. Why is their argument valid? What argument could there be for them to sell their home and move to a different city?

2. **Use Visual Information** Use an example from the graph of the different grocery items and their changes in price to explain the concept of inflation.

Price Indexes: Text

3. **Draw Conclusions** How are most people likely to adjust their spending when prices for consumer goods are rising?

4. **Categorize** Place the following items into a category in the CPI Market Basket: toothpaste, a bicycle, a book, prescription sunglasses, shoes, a banana, and a trip to the movies.

5. **Analyze Interactions** How are the CPI and the rate of inflation related? Explain how the CPI affects the rate of inflation.

6. **Cite Evidence** The core inflation rate was developed to exclude some economic data. What information supports the logic behind the development of the core inflation rate?

Identifying Causes of Inflation: Text

7. **Identify Cause and Effect** As you read "Identifying Causes of Inflation" and "Interpreting Effects of Inflation," use this graphic organizer to record the causes and effects of inflation.

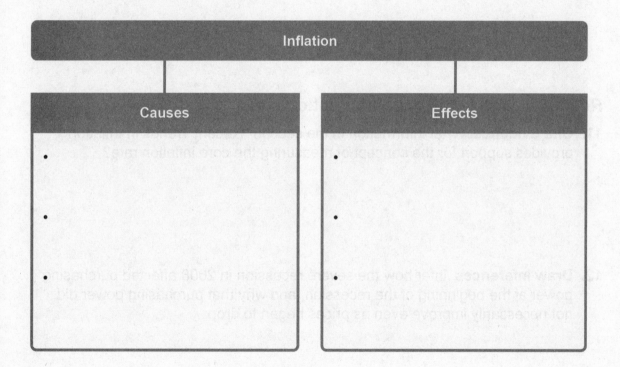

8. **Use Visual Information** Refer to the Wage-Price Spiral illustration. How could you modify the illustration to include the effects of low unemployment on the wage-price spiral?

Interactive Reading Notepad • Lesson 7.5

Interpreting Effects of Inflation: Text

9. **Summarize** Explain why inflation sometimes, but not always, erodes income.

10. **Assess an Argument** Lydia has $1,000 in her savings account. Currently, the rate of inflation is 3 percent, and the interest rate on her savings account is 4 percent. She has decided that if the rate of inflation goes above 3 percent, she will take her money out of her savings account because she won't be making any money in interest. Is her argument valid? Explain.

Recent Trends in the Rate of Inflation: Text

11. **Cite Evidence** What information in the section "Recent Trends in Inflation" provides support for the concept of measuring the core inflation rate?

12. **Draw Inferences** Infer how the severe recession in 2008 affected purchasing power at the beginning of the recession, and why that purchasing power did not necessarily improve even as prices began to drop.

Lesson 7.6 Poverty and Income Distribution

Key Terms

poverty threshold

poverty rate

income distribution

food stamp program

Lorenz Curve

enterprise zone

block grants

workfare

cash transfers

in-kind benefits

medical benefits

grant

Academic Vocabulary

Demographic: relating to the study of the human characteristics of populations

Per capita: per person

Subsidies: monetary help given by the government to a person or group to support the public interest

---

Lesson Objectives

1 **Define** who is poor, according to government standards.

2 **Describe** the causes of poverty.

3 **Analyze** the distribution of income in the United States.

4 **Analyze** the costs and benefits of U.S. economic policy related to the goal of equity.

Living in Poverty: Text

1. **Summarize** How do we measure poverty in the United States?

What Causes Poverty?: Text

2. **Draw Conclusions** Is it possible for someone to work full time and still be poor?

3. **Categorize** What are the most recognized causes of poverty?

Household Income: Text

4.   Determine Central Ideas What does income distribution tell economists?

5.   Identify Supporting Details The wealthiest fifth of American households earned more income (50.5 percent) than the bottom four fifths combined. Why are there such differences in income among Americans?

The Economic Goal of Equity: Text

6.   Summarize What kinds of assistance might a family living in poverty be able to get from the government?

7. **Summarize** In the center of the word web, you will see the phrase "redistribution programs." Draw as many lines out as you can to fill in the types of redistribution programs.

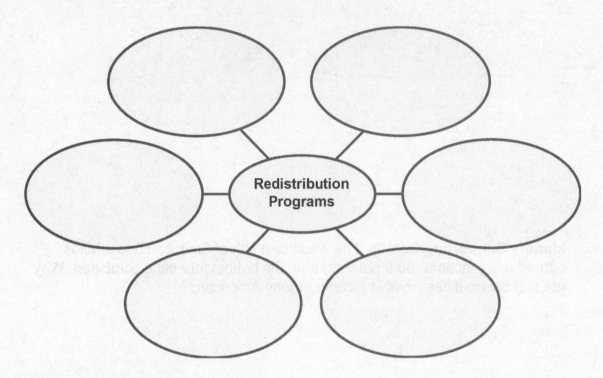

Charitable Donations: Text

8. **Compare and Contrast** Reread the paragraph about President George W. Bush's plan that allowed religious organizations to compete for federal funds. Why were some people in favor of it and other people against it?

Lesson 8.1 Understanding Taxes

Key Terms

tax   tax base
revenue   individual income tax
progressive tax   corporate income tax
proportional tax   property tax
regressive tax   incidence of a tax
sales tax

Academic Vocabulary

Burden: something that is carried or borne

Provision: a requirement established by law

Welfare: the good fortune or well-being of a person or group

Lesson Objectives

1 **Identify** the sources of the government's authority to tax in the U.S. Constitution.

2 **Describe** types of tax bases and tax structures.

3 **Identify** who bears the burden of a tax.

4 **Describe** the key characteristics of a tax.

The Importance of National Taxes: Text

1. **Identify Cause and Effect** As you read the section "The Importance of National Taxes," consider what might happen if the government cut taxes drastically.

2. **Draw Conclusions** Read "The Impact of Taxation." Why do you think the majority of American citizens consent to have their earnings taxed by the government?

3. **Identify Supporting Details** Explain the impact of taxation on the United States economy.

4. **Draw Inferences** After reading "Limits on the Power to Tax," explain why you think the Framers of the Constitution placed limits on the government's power to tax.

Tax Structures and Tax Bases: Text

5. **Vocabulary: Use Context Clues** Use context clues about the nature of progressive taxes to come up with a definition of the word *progressive*.

6. **Compare and Contrast** How are progressive, proportional, and regressive taxes similar? How are they different? Use evidence from the text to support your answer.

7. **Draw Inferences** What is meant when a community is said to have a "strong tax base"?

The Tax Burden: Text

8. **Integrate Information From Diverse Sources** After reading "The Tax Burden" and examining the illustrations, explain who you think would bear the tax burden of an excise tax on a cup of coffee purchased at a coffee shop.

9. **Identify Supporting Details** How would you describe the demand for a product whose consumers bear the burden of an excise tax on that product?

Key Characteristics of a Tax: Text

10. **Identify Supporting Details** One of the characteristics of a good tax is certainty, which includes knowing when a tax is due. When are income taxes in the United States due?

11. **Explain an Argument** Read "Determining Equity." What do you think a supporter of the benefits-received principle might say about progressive taxation?

12. **Summarize** Complete this graphic organizer about the basic structures and key characteristics of taxes.

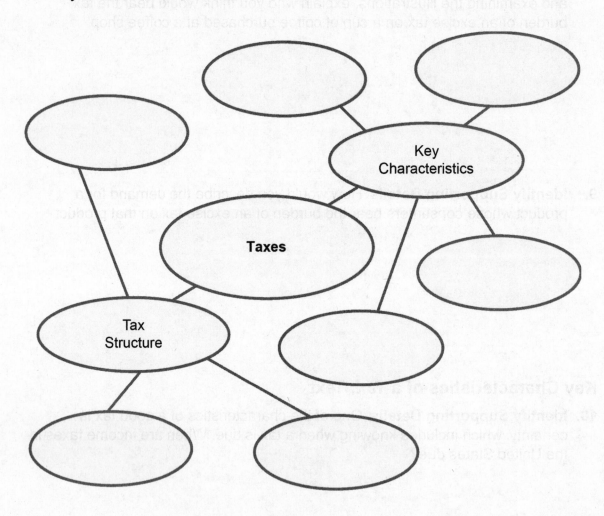

Lesson 8.2 Federal Taxes

Key Terms

direct tax	indirect tax
withholding	estate tax
tax return	gift tax
taxable income	tax incentive
personal exemption	tax deduction
tax credit	tariffs

Academic Vocabulary

Heir: a person who is entitled to inherit the estate of someone

Installment: one in a series of something

Lesson Objectives

1 **Identify** the basic characteristics and importance of individual and corporate income taxes at the national level.

2 **Explain** the purpose and importance of Social Security, Medicare, and unemployment taxes.

3 **Identify** other types of taxes levied at the national level.

Individual and Corporate Income Taxes: Text

1. **Identify Supporting Details** As you read this Lesson, use this graphic organizer to record details about different types of taxes.

Type of Tax	Description
Individual Income	
Corporate Income	
Social Insurance	
Excise	
Estate	
Gift	
Import	

2. **Summarize** As you read "Individual Income Taxes," summarize the reasons that individuals essentially pay their taxes all throughout the year rather than all at once.

3. **Use Visual Information** Look at the tax schedule in Figure 8.5. Assume you are a single person to whom this schedule applies who made $40,000 in taxable income in a year. What would your income tax be?

4. **Identify Supporting Details** Read "Filing a Tax Return." What are some steps a person can take to reduce his or her taxable income?

Social Security, Medicare, and Unemployment Taxes: Text

5. **Determine Central Ideas** As you read this section, identify the common purpose of Social Security, Medicare, and unemployment taxes.

6. **Contrast** Read the sections "Social Security Taxes" and "Medicare Taxes." Explain how these two taxes differ in their structure.

Other National Taxes: Text

7. **Paraphrase** Read the sections "Estate Taxes" and "Gift Taxes." Explain how these two taxes are related to one another.

8. **Summarize** Read "Taxes That Affect Behavior," and summarize how taxes and related incentives are used to change people's behavior.

Lesson 8.3 Federal Spending

Key Terms

mandatory spending   entitlement

discretionary spending

Academic Vocabulary

Denounce: to criticize

Dilemma: a situation with unsatisfactory, but necessary, choices

---

Lesson Objectives

1 **Analyze** categories of expenditures in the U.S. federal budget.

2 **Describe** major entitlement programs.

3 **Identify** major types of discretionary spending in the federal budget.

Mandatory and Discretionary Spending: Text

1. **Analyze Interactions** As you read the section "Mandatory and Discretionary Spending," note how mandatory spending affects discretionary spending.

2. **Draw Inferences** Read the definition of *mandatory spending* in the fourth paragraph of "Mandatory and Discretionary Spending." What has to happen for the amount that Congress spends on mandatory spending to change?

3. **Draw Conclusions** Look at Figure 8.6. Why do you think that the percentage of federal spending that is mandatory has grown in recent years?

Government Entitlements: Text

4. **Vocabulary: Use Context Clues** Note the term *means-tested* that is used in the first line of the second paragraph under "Government Entitlements." Define this term in your own words using context clues.

5. **Distinguish Among Fact, Opinion, and Reasoned Judgment** Read the section entitled "Social Security." What is the reason for the statement that Social Security faces an uncertain future? Explain why you think this is a fact, an opinion, or a reasoned judgment.

6. **Compare and Contrast** Read the sections "Medicare" and "Medicaid." How are Medicare and Medicaid different and similar?

7. **Determine Central Ideas** Consider all you have read about the mandatory spending programs in this section. What do you think is the overriding goal of the government in providing these programs?

Spending on Discretionary Programs: Text

8. **Categorize** Use this chart to classify federal spending as mandatory or discretionary as you finish the Lesson.

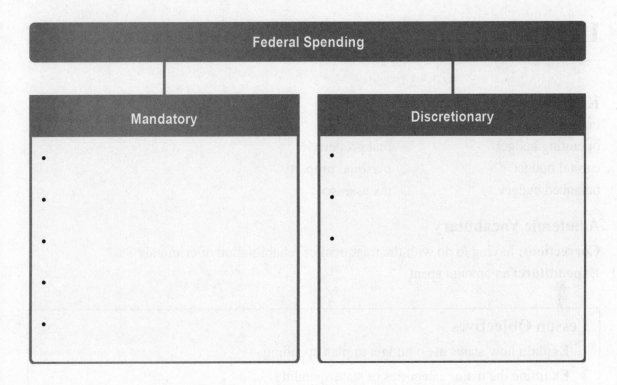

Federal Spending

Mandatory	Discretionary
•	•
•	•
•	•
•	
•	

9. **Explain** Why do you think defense spending is categorized as discretionary, rather than mandatory, spending, even though millions of people are part of the armed services or employed in defense?

10. **Draw Conclusions** Why do you think the federal government imposes guidelines on federal grants-in-aid?

Lesson 8.4 State and Local Taxes and Spending

Key Terms

budget

operating budget

capital budget

balanced budget

tax exempt

real property

personal property

tax assessor

Academic Vocabulary

Corrections: having to do with the treatment or rehabilitation of criminals

Expenditure: an amount spent

Lesson Objectives

1 **Explain** how states use a budget to plan spending.

2 **Examine** the major categories of state spending.

3 **Identify** the types and economic importance of state taxes.

4 **Describe** local government, and the types and economic importance of local taxes.

Budgeting at the State Level: Text

1. **Summarize** As you read this section and the ones that follow, complete the following diagram. Add more bullets as needed.

State and Local Revenue Collection	State and Local Spending
•	•
•	•
•	•
•	•
•	•
•	•
•	•
•	•

2. **Categorize** Read the sections "Operating Budgets" and "Capital Budgets." Now, suppose your state wanted to build a new public hospital to serve a rural area. From which budget—operating or capital—would this project be funded? Explain your answer.

3. **Cite Evidence** Read the section "Balancing State Budgets." Explain why it is easier for a state government to balance its overall budget than it is for the federal government to do so.

State Spending Categories: Text

4. **Draw Conclusions** Why does every state support at least one public university? What benefit does the state receive from this expense?

5. **Draw Inferences** Read the section "Public Safety." Why do you think states typically fund a state crime lab?

6. **Identify Supporting Details** After reading "State Spending Categories," consider this statement: "Modern government is a cooperative effort between federal, state, and local governments." Find details in this section to support this statement.

Revenue for State Budgets: Text

7. **Analyze Interactions** Read the section "Sales and Excise Taxes." Suppose your state collects a sales tax, but a bordering state does not. A number of people cross the border each day in order to shop without paying sales tax. What must state officials consider when thinking about how to react to this situation?

8. **Draw Inferences** Look at Figure 8.9 and the map "State Individual Income Taxes." Note that some states collect no individual income tax, or only a very small one. What can you infer about the sources of revenue in those states?

Local Government Spending and Revenue: Text

9. **Summarize** Read the section "The Jobs of Local Government." How would you characterize the kinds of services that local governments provide—and how are they different from the services provided by the federal government?

10. **Draw Inferences** Read the section "Other Local Taxes." Why do you think residents of a place like New York City might be willing to tolerate higher taxes for their restaurants and hotels?

Lesson 9.1 The Federal Budget and Fiscal Policy

Key Terms

fiscal policy

federal budget

fiscal year

appropriations bill

expansionary policy

contractionary policy

Academic Vocabulary

Modify: to change or alter

Resolution: a formal statement made by an assembly

Alternative: option

Lesson Objectives

1 **Describe** how the federal budget is created.

2 **Analyze** the impact of expansionary and contractionary fiscal policy on the economy.

3 **Identify** the limits of fiscal policy.

The Federal Budget and Fiscal Policy: Text

1. **Determine Central Ideas** Read the section "Fiscal Policy." Explain how you think fiscal policy works to expand or slow economic growth, achieve employment, and maintain price stability.

2. **Explain an Argument** Read the section "Federal Budget Basics." Using your own words, explain why you think the federal budget reflects the nation's priorities.

3. **Draw Inferences** Review Figure 9.2, which summarizes how the federal budget is created. Why do you think the process shown here is so much affected by the relationship between the President and Congress?

How Fiscal Policy Decisions Impact the Economy: Text

4. **Compare and Contrast** How does expansionary fiscal policy compare to contractionary fiscal policy? Use this graphic organizer to record the key ideas from this section.

Fiscal Policies		
	Expansionary	**Contractionary**
Purpose		
Methods		
Desired results		

5. **Use Visual Information** Look at Figure 9.6. How does this graph explain why the government's fiscal policy is an effective tool for influencing the overall economy?

The Limits and Costs of Fiscal Policy: Text

6. **Integrate Information From Diverse Sources** Read the quote by Professor David N. Weil. Then look at Figure 9.7. Explain how the timeline agrees or disagrees with Professor Weil's observation.

7. **Explain an Argument** Review the section "Political Pressures." The federal government is not required to balance its budget, and it almost always spends more than it earns in taxes and other revenue. It borrows money to pay for the difference. As a result, the U.S. federal government has accumulated trillions of dollars in debt. Explain how political pressure contributes to this problem.

Lesson 9.2 Fiscal Policy Options

Key Terms

classical economics

John Maynard Keynes

productive capacity

demand-side economics

Keynesian economics

multiplier effect

automatic stabilizers

supply-side economics

Arthur Laffer

deficit spending

John Kenneth Galbraith

Milton Friedman

Academic Vocabulary

Breadwinner: the person in a family who earns the main income

---

Lesson Objectives

1 **Compare** and contrast classical economics and demand-side economics.

2 **Analyze** the importance of John Maynard Keynes and his economic theories.

3 **Explain** the basic principles of supply-side economics and the importance of Milton Friedman.

4 **Analyze** the impact of fiscal policy decisions on the economy of the United States.

Classical Economics: Text

1. **Identify Cause and Effect** What do classical economists believe happens during a recession as a result of people acting in their own self-interest?

2. **Determine Author's Purpose** In the section "Classical Economics," read John Maynard Keynes's response to the classical view that in the long run, markets would return to equilibrium: "In the long run we are all dead." How did Keynes's comment highlight a problem with classical economics?

Keynesian Economics: Text

3. **Summarize** Read the section "Changing Government's Role in the Economy." What was Keynes's solution for motivating businesses to increase production during the Great Depression?

4. **Explain an Argument** According to the Keynesian theory of economics, how would expansionary fiscal policy decrease the unemployment rate during a recession?

5. **Determine Central Ideas** In the section "Avoiding Recession," you will read about some classical economists' criticism of Franklin Roosevelt's demand-side approach to ending the Great Depression. What was the basis of this criticism?

6. **Identify Key Steps in a Process** What is the first step that government takes to trigger the multiplier effect?

Supply-Side Economics: Text

7. **Determine Central Ideas** Read the first sentence of "Supply-Side Economics." Faced with an economy falling into recession, what would supply-side economists likely encourage the government to do?

8. **Summarize** Look at Figure 9.14. What is the basic message behind the Laffer curve?

The Recent History of U.S. Fiscal Policy: Text

9. **Draw Inferences** How did the government attempt to manage the economy for three decades after World War II as a result of Keynes's influence?

10. **Analyze Interactions** Ronald Reagan, with the advice of Milton Friedman, developed economic policies that mixed classical and supply-side theories. What effect did that have on Keynesian theory?

11. **Cite Evidence** Was President Obama's stimulus program a success? Explain your answer.

Lesson 9.3 The National Debt and Deficits

Key Terms

budget surplus

budget deficit

Treasury bill

Treasury note

Treasury bond

national debt

crowding-out effect

Academic Vocabulary

Exceed: to go beyond or above

Circulation: movement of something through a system

Undertake: to accept responsibility for doing some task or function

Outweigh: to become greater or more important than something else

Substantially: significantly, or by a large amount

Lesson Objectives

1 **Explain** the importance of balancing the budget.

2 **Analyze** the impact of fiscal policy decisions on the nation's economy.

3 **Summarize** the way budget deficits add to the national debt.

4 **Identify** how political leaders have tried to control the deficit.

Budget Surpluses and Deficits: Text

1. **Identify Cause and Effect** As you read "The National Debt and Deficits," use this graphic organizer to list the causes and effects of a budget deficit.

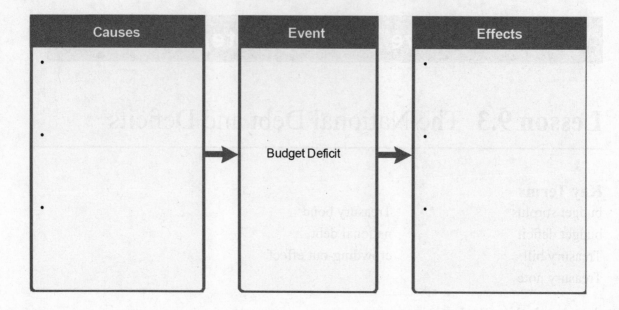

Causes	Event	Effects
•		•
•	Budget Deficit	•
•		•

2. **Analyze Explanations** Read the first paragraphs under "Budget Surpluses and Deficits." What explains the existence of a budget deficit?

3. **Use Visual Information** Look at figure 9.18. What conclusion can you draw about the challenges of balancing the budget?

Deficits and the National Debt: Text

4. **Determine Central Ideas** What is the difference between a budget deficit and the national debt?

5. **Summarize** Read the section "Measuring the National Debt." How has the U.S. economy changed in recent times?

6. **Identify Key Steps in a Process** How does the United States borrow the money it borrows when it runs a deficit?

The Impact of Debt: Text

7. **Summarize** Read the section "Problems of a National Debt." Explain the three main problems that can arise from a national debt.

8. **Compare Authors' Points of View** Look at Figure 9.21. Summarize the two views about the impact of debt presented there.

Measures to Control the Deficit: Text

9. **Draw Inferences** Read the section "Reducing Deficits." Why do you think some people have favored passing laws or even amending the Constitution in order to limit deficits?

10. **Identify Key Steps in a Process** Read the section "The Surpluses of the Late 1990s." What steps led to the brief period of government surpluses?

11. **Identify Cause and Effect** The section "A Return to Deficit Spending" explains why the surpluses of the late 1990s did not last. What were the key causes of this development?

Interactive Reading Notepad

Lesson 9.4 Monetary Policy Options

Key Terms

money creation

required reserve ratio

money multiplier formula

excess reserves

discount rate

federal funds rate

prime rate

open market operations

security

Academic Vocabulary

Manipulate: to influence or cause the behavior of something or someone else

Initial: the first

Disruptive: causing disorder

Lesson Objectives

1 **Describe** the process of money creation.

2 **Analyze** how the Federal Reserve uses reserve requirements to implement U.S. monetary policy.

3 **Analyze** the three primary tools the Federal Reserve uses to implement monetary policy, including open market operations.

4 **Explain** why the Federal Reserve prefers open market operations as a means to implementing monetary policy.

Creating Money: Text

1. **Summarize** As you read this lesson, use the graphic organizer to describe the tools the Federal Reserve uses to manipulate the money supply.

Manipulating the Money Supply		
Tools	**To Increase It**	**To Decrease It**
Reserve requirements		
Discount rate		
Open market operations		

2. **Compare and Contrast** Read "Money Manufacture vs. Money Creation," and then "How Banks Create Money." Then summarize the difference between money manufacture and money creation.

3. **Identify Key Steps in a Process** Look at Figure 9.23, and explain how a $1,000 deposit can increase the money supply by $2,710.

Monetary Tool #1: Reserve Requirements: Text

4. **Paraphrase** (a) Why does the Fed prefer not to use reserve requirements to adjust the money supply? (b) Under what circumstances might the Fed decide to change the reserve requirement?

Monetary Tool #2: The Discount Rate: Text

5. **Identify Central Ideas** If the discount rate rose, would you expect the prime rate to rise or fall? Why?

6. **Draw Inferences** Read the second paragraph under "Monetary Tool #2: The Discount Rate." Why do you think the Federal Reserve changes the federal funds rate by setting targets and taking steps to work toward them?

7. **Draw Conclusions** (a) How are the discount rate and the federal funds rate different? (b) Why does the Fed keep the discount rate higher than the federal funds rate?

Monetary Tool #3: Open Market Operations: Text

8. **Determine Central Ideas** Of the three basic monetary tools, which one does the Fed use most commonly? Why?

Interactive Reading Notepad • Lesson 9.4

9. **Paraphrase** Read the quote from the publication "What Are Open Market Operations?" Restate this quote in your own words, including the purpose beyond the process described.

Using Monetary Policy Tools: Text

10. **Draw Inferences** (a) When the Fed cuts interest rates, what effect does it expect to have on business and consumers? (b) How is the Fed influenced by market forces in making rate decisions?

Lesson 9.5 The Effects of Monetary Policy

Key Terms

easy money policy

tight money policy

inside lag

outside lag

monetarism

Friedrich Hayek

Academic Vocabulary

Intensify: make stronger

Reluctant: less than willing

Lesson Objectives

1 **Explain** how monetary policy works.

2 **Describe** how the timing of monetary policy can impact business cycles and key economic indicators.

3 **Analyze** the costs and benefits of monetary policy in terms of economic growth.

4 **Contrast** two general approaches to monetary policy.

The Basics of Monetary Policy: Text

1. **Analyze Interactions** Read the first paragraph of "How Money Supply Impacts Interest Rates." Now suppose that you have been saving money for a down payment on a house. If interest rates fall, would you be more or less likely to buy a house? Explain your answer.

2. **Use Visual Information** Look at Figure 9.27. Now suppose you are a member of the Federal Reserve and observe that GDP is basically holding steady and unemployment is creeping up. Would you recommend increasing the money supply, decreasing it, or leaving it the same? Why? What do you hope will happen?

Timing Monetary Policy: Text

3. **Paraphrase** Review the subsections "The Results of Good Timing" and "The Results of Bad Timing" and Figure 9.28. If the typical business cycle were a roller coaster, how would it feel to ride without any intervention from the Fed? How would it feel if the Fed timed monetary policy well? What would it be like if the Fed timed monetary policy badly?

4. **Compare and Contrast** Review the subsections "Inside Lags" and "Outside Lags." Using this graphic organizer, indicate whether each delay would be considered an inside lag or an outside lag by circling the correct answer.

Examples	Inside/Outside Lag
• GDP data takes months to collect.	
• FOMC meeting postponed.	
• Business orders design for new factory .	
• Revised unemployment data show slow job growth last year .	
• Corporate board approves plans for new stores.	

Anticipating Business Cycles: Text

5. **Analyze Interactions** Read the section "How Monetary Policy Affects Inflation." Pay close attention to how different monetary policies interact with inflation and contraction in the economy. Then write a brief summary of why this interaction is complicated.

6. **Draw Conclusions** Read the third paragraph in the section "How Monetary Policy Affects Inflation." What conclusion does the text suggest given the challenges of timing monetary policy?

7. **Using Visual Information** Take a look at Figure 9.30. What does this timeline suggest about the nature of recessions in the United States in recent history?

Debating Monetary Policy: Text

8. **Compare and Contrast** Read this section and write a brief summary of how the influential economists Keynes, Friedman, and Hayek viewed the use of monetary policy.

Lesson 10.1 Why Nations Trade

Key Terms

export

import

absolute advantage

comparative advantage

law of comparative advantage

interdependence

Academic Vocabulary

Extract: to remove from something, such as mineral resources taken from the earth

Network: a system of interconnected elements that facilitates work processes, transportation, or communication

Capable: having the ability to do something

Range: extent of something from one limit to another; variety

Estimate: approximated amount; projection based on available data

Access: ability to obtain

Lesson Objectives

1 **Evaluate** the impact of the unequal distribution of resources.

2 **Analyze** the concepts of specialization and comparative advantage to explain why nations trade.

3 **Summarize** the position of the United States in world trade.

4 **Describe** the effects of trade on employment.

Resource Distribution and Specialization: Text

1. **Summarize** How are the factors of production related to the need to specialize?

2. **Describe** How is specialization related to trade?

3. **Identify** Use the graphic organizer to identify the causes and effects of resource distribution.

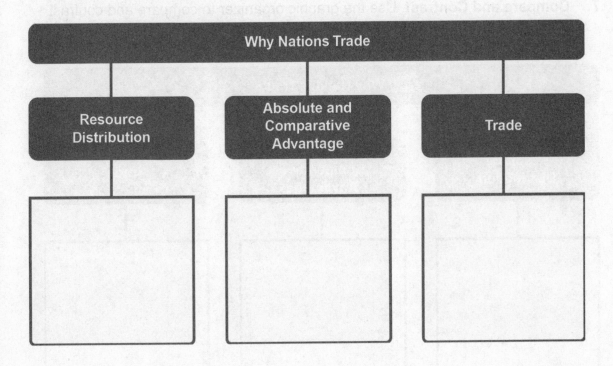

Absolute and Comparative Advantage: Text

4. **Define** What is absolute advantage, and how is it related to resource use?

5. **Define** What is comparative advantage, and how is it related to opportunity cost?

6. **Synthesize** Why does the law of comparative advantage make sense based on resource use?

7. **Compare and Contrast** Use the graphic organizer to compare and contrast absolute and comparative advantage.

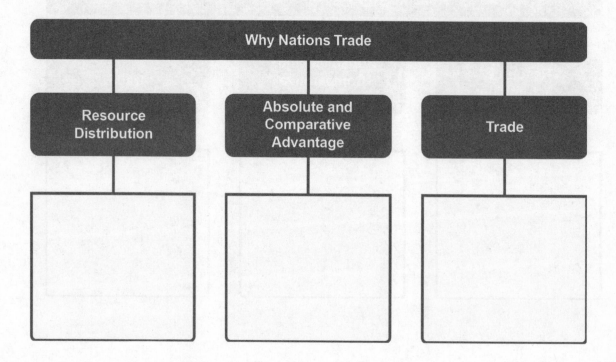

8. **Connect** How does following the law of comparative advantage result in mutual benefit?

Comparative Advantage and World Trade: Text

9. **Identify Cause and Effect** Why does trade result in interdependence?

10. **Identify Central Ideas** Use the graphic organizer to identify the causes and effects of trade.

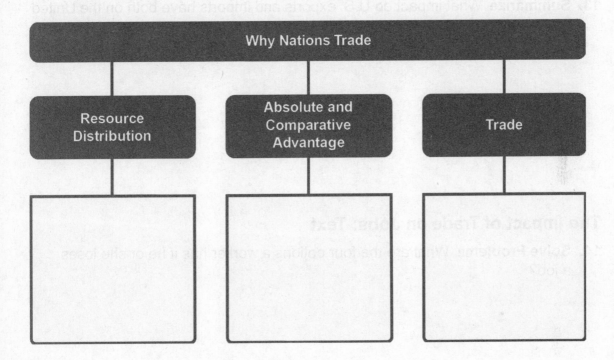

The United States and Its Trading Partners: Text

11. **Identify** Where does the United States rank among countries as an importer and exporter?

12. **Identify** What countries are the leading trading partners of the United States?

13. **Summarize** What impact do U.S. exports and imports have both on the United States and on its trading partners?

The Impact of Trade on Jobs: Text

14. **Solve Problems** What are the four options a worker has if he or she loses a job?

15. **Infer** Why do governments institute retraining programs to help workers who lose jobs?

Lesson 10.2 Trade Barriers and Agreements

Key Terms

trade barrier

tariff

import quota

sanctions

embargo

trade war

protectionism

infant industry

free trade

World Trade Organization

free trade zone

Academic Vocabulary

Erect: construct

Impose: force something unfamiliar or unwanted to be accepted

Lesson Objectives

1 **Describe** the policies nations use to control or direct international trade.

2 **Analyze** the effects of international trade agreements.

3 **Summarize** the arguments for and against free international trade.

4 **Explain** the role of multinational corporations in the process of globalization.

Free Trade and Trade Barriers: Text

1. **Compare and Contrast** How are import quotas and tariffs similar?

2. **Identify Cause and Effect** How do tariffs on U.S. goods benefit U.S. consumers?

3. **Vocabulary: Use Context Clues** How would you define *embargo* based on context clues in the following sentence? "The purpose of this embargo was to reduce trade and weaken Cuba's communist government."

Effects of Trade Barriers: Text

4. **Analyze Interactions** How did the free trade agreements in place today grow out of the major trade wars of the past?

Arguments for Protectionism: Text

5. **Draw Inferences** What reasons might local political leaders have to want to protect jobs in their area?

6. **Assess an Argument** Choose one argument against protecting infant industries. Then assess the argument, describing whether you believe it is valid and whether it is a strong enough argument to eliminate protections for infant industries.

7. **Distinguish Among Fact, Opinion, and Reasoned Judgment** An argument in favor of protectionism is that certain industries require protection because their products are essential to defending the country. An argument against this kind of protectionism is that raises costs for consumers. What is your opinion on how to determine whether a company deserves protection?

Trade Agreements: Text

8. **Identify Cause and Effect** How did the Smoot-Hawley Act lead to free trade?

9. **Categorize** Use the graphic organizer to categorize the arguments for trade barriers and for trade agreements.

Arguments	
For Trade Barriers	**For Trade Agreements**
• Jobs: • Domestic industries:	• Competition: • Trade Organizations:

Regional Trade Organizations: Text

10. Evaluate Explanations Some countries are not currently EU members but are candidates for membership. What are some reasons a country would want to join the EU?

11. Assess an Argument Some people are concerned that free trade agreements give too much economic power to large multinational corporations. Do you think this argument is valid? Explain.

The Role of Multinationals: Text

12. Analyze Interactions Think about the characteristics of a corporation. How might these characteristics make it easier for a company to become multinational?

Lesson 10.3 Exchange Rates and Trade

Key Terms

exchange rate	flexible exchange-rate system
appreciation	balance of trade
depreciation	trade surplus
foreign exchange market	trade deficit
fixed exchange-rate system	balance of payments

Academic Vocabulary

Value: the relative worth of something

Exchange: to give up something for an item of equivalent value

Stabilization: the process of maintaining something at a given, steady level

---

Lesson Objectives

1 **Analyze** the effects of changes in exchange rates on world trade.

2 **Define** *balance of trade.*

3 **Summarize** the effects of international trade on the United States and its trading partners.

4 **Analyze** the role of the United States in international trade.

Foreign Exchange and Currencies: Text

1. **Draw Inferences** Suppose you traveled to Mexico before exchange rates had been established. What would the impact of this be?

2. **Identify Cause and Effect** What would the impact of a weak dollar be on tourism to the United States? Why?

3. Draw Conclusions Do you think a merchant in a country with a weak currency would accept payment with a U.S. dollar? Why?

4. Categorize Use the graphic organizer to explain how exchange rates affect trade.

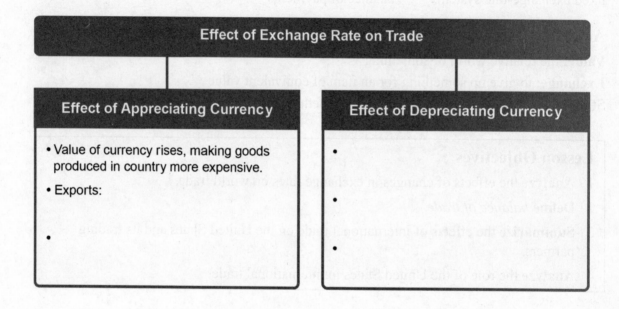

Effect of Exchange Rate on Trade

Effect of Appreciating Currency	Effect of Depreciating Currency
• Value of currency rises, making goods produced in country more expensive. • Exports: •	• • •

Determining the Value of Currency: Text

5. **Contrast** How is the fixed exchange-rate system different from the flexible exchange-rate system?

6. **Integrate Information From Diverse Sources** Why were the economy and currency of the United States the strongest in the world after World War II?

7. **Assess an Argument** Some people have argued that the United States, Canada, and Mexico should form a single currency like the euro. Do you agree or disagree with this argument? Why or why not?

Balance of Trade: Text

8. **Cite Evidence** What happens to the value of a country's currency when it imports more than it exports over an extended period of time? Provide an example.

9. **Draw Conclusions** Suppose a German businessperson invested in a German car company such as Volkswagen. Would that investment be factored into Germany's balance of payments? Explain.

A Growing Trade Deficit: Text

10. **Integrate Information From Diverse Sources** What changes to the U.S. economy have contributed to the shift in the United States' balance of trade?

11. **Draw Inferences** The United States is one of the world's largest exporters of wheat. If a drought in the Midwest destroyed many wheat crops, how might that affect the United States' trade deficit?

Interactive Reading Notepad

Lesson 10.4 Development

Key Terms

development

developed nation

less developed country

newly industrialized country

per capita GDP

industrialization

literacy rate

life expectancy

infant mortality rate

subsistence agriculture

Academic Vocabulary

Per capita: for each person; literally, "by heads"

Urbanization: the increasing number of a nation's population that lives in cities

Subsistence: the minimum amount of food, clothing, or other essential things needed to stay alive

---

Lesson Objectives

1 **Summarize** the concept of economic development.

2 **Identify** the characteristics of developed and less developed countries.

3 **Explain** the use of GDP and other measurements of economic development.

Development Around the World: Text

1. **Cite Evidence** Identify some aspects of the average American's life that reflect the high level of development of the United States.

2. **Draw Conclusions** How do the economic advances made by developed countries help the newly industrialized countries (NICs) make progress more quickly?

Indicators of Development: Text

3. **Summarize** As you read "Indicators of Development," fill in this graphic organizer. Add as many bulleted items as you wish.

Indicators of Development			
Per Capita GDP	Energy Use	Consumer Goods	Social Indicators
• Rising GDP generally provides higher standard of living.			• Higher literacy rate reflects better education opportunities.

4. **Draw Inferences** China's gross domestic product ranks second only to that of the United States. Why do economists still consider China a less developed country?

5. **Assess an Argument** Two countries have the same per capita GDP. Some economists claim that having equal per capita GDPs does not necessarily mean that the people of the two countries are equally well off. Do you agree? Why or why not?

6. **Explain an Argument** An LDC has plans to institute a program to build wells and water purification facilities in rural communities. Why might a supporter argue that such a program could enhance the country's rate of development?

Indicators of Developed Nations: Text

7. **Identify Key Steps in a Process** How does a less developed country, with a traditional economy, turn itself into a developed country?

8. **Evaluate Explanations** Why does the statistic that American households have, on average, more than two cars indicate that the country is developed?

9. **Distinguish Among Fact, Opinion, and Reasoned Judgment** Read the following quotation, and then answer the question.

"New technologies are making the profession of farming more efficient."

Why is this so?

Indicators of Less Developed Nations: Text

10. Compare and Contrast What are the main differences between agriculture in a developed nation and agriculture in a less developed country (LDC)?

Lesson 10.5 Growth, Resources, and Development

Key Terms

population growth rate

malnutrition

internal financing

foreign investment

foreign direct investment

foreign portfolio investment

debt rescheduling

stabilization program

nongovernmental organization

Academic Vocabulary

Illiteracy: the inability to read or write

Increased life expectancy: An increase in the expected length of life among a given set of people

Migrate: move from one area or country to settle in another

Outpace: to move faster than another person or thing

Social unrest: rebellion or refusal to obey law and order in a society or nation

Foreign aid: money, food, or other resources given by one nation to another

---

Lesson Objectives

1 **Summarize** major issues that affect international economic development.

2 **Describe** the role of government in promoting or hindering national economic development.

3 **Summarize** the role of international investment and foreign aid in economic development.

4 **Analyze** the functions of international economic institutions in the global economy.

A Growing Population: Text

1. **Compare and Contrast** According to the Lesson, the population growth rate for less developed countries is estimated to be around 1.8 percent. Why is this number, which seems to be low, really quite high, and what does this mean for the world's future population?

2. **Draw Inferences** What do you think the United States' population growth rate of 0.7 might mean for you in the future? How could it affect the economies of the United States and other developed countries?

Obstacles to Development: Text

3. **Vocabulary: Use Context Clues** Read "Educating and Training Growing Populations." What is meant by the term *human capital*? Why is human capital necessary to move beyond mere subsistence?

4. **Draw Inferences** What does physical geography have to do with a nation's status as an LDC?

Interactive Reading Notepad • Lesson 10.5

Political Barriers to Growth: Text

5. **Analyze Interactions** How do political factors lead to or exacerbate a nation's standing as an LDC? Do you think there are things that can be done to alter or change this?

6. **Draw Inferences** In this Lesson, you read about the World Bank's work with Burundi. How might this work help Burundi to climb out of LDC status?

Finance and Development: Text

7. **Summarize** Why do so many LDCs have so little capital available from internal financing?

8. **Vocabulary: Use Context Clues** This Lesson talks about foreign direct investment and foreign portfolio investment. Differentiate between the two. Is either one more advantageous or beneficial?

Promoting Development: Text

9. Vocabulary: Use Context Clues How do organizations like the IMF use debt rescheduling in their efforts to assist LDCs?

10. Categorize Use the graphic organizer to categorize what you have learned about the factors affecting development.

Factors Affecting Development	
Factor	**Effect**
Population Growth	High rate of population growth presents challenges to development.
Physical capital	
Human capital	• Education and training is needed for people to develop skills and adapt to changing technology. • •
Political factors	
Economic factors	Large loans can lead to spiraling debt.

Interactive Reading Notepad

Lesson 10.6 Changing Economies

Key Terms
privatization
special economic zone

Academic Vocabulary
Pension: a sum of money paid regularly as a retirement benefit
Shambles: a scene of complete disorder or ruin

Lesson Objectives
1 **Identify** the characteristics of economic transition.
2 **Summarize** the political and economic changes experienced by Russia since the fall of communism.
3 **Analyze** the reasons for economic growth in China and India in recent years.
4 **Identify** the economic challenges faced by developing nations in Africa and Latin America.

Moving Toward a Market Economy: Text

1. **Identify Key Steps in a Process** What steps can a government take to privatize businesses?

2. **Identify Supporting Details** Why do there need to be changes in the legal system when transitioning to a market economy?

Changes in Russia: Text

3. **Categorize** Complete the word web with words associated with Russia as it transitioned to a market economy.

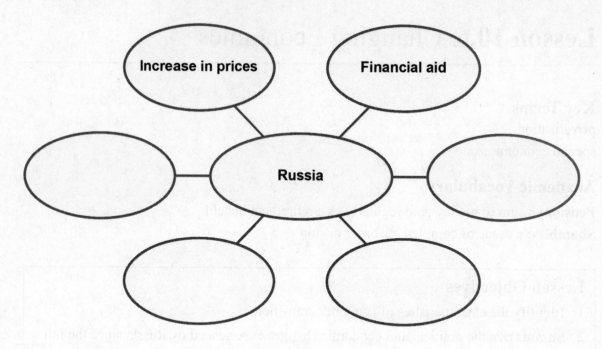

4. **Cite Evidence** Describe Russia's economy in the twenty-first century.

Growth in Asia Through Trade: Text

5. **Identify Cause and Effect** What was the effect of Deng Xiaoping's economic policies?

6. **Draw Conclusions** What difficulties does China face due to its rapid development?

7. **Determine Author's Point of View** Gurcharan Das, an Indian business executive, said, "When half the population in a society is middle class, its politics will change." What do you think he meant?

Growth and Challenges in Africa and Latin America: Text

8. **Categorize** What are the economic advantages and political challenges to growth in Nigeria?

9. **Identify Supporting Details** Why is sugar important to Brazil's economy?

10. **Determine Central Ideas** How might Mexico's location and climate play a role in its large tourism industry?

Lesson 10.7 Globalization

Key Terms

globalization

offshoring

remittances

"brain drain"

sustainable development

deforestation

renewable resources

nonrenewable resources

Academic Vocabulary

Bloc: a group formed to promote certain interests

Contamination: the process of making something dirty or polluted

Dwindling: growing steadily smaller

Lesson Objectives

1 **Define** *globalization,* and summarize the factors that have led to its spread.

2 **Identify** challenges created by globalization.

3 **Analyze** the benefits of globalization.

4 **Summarize** the effects of globalization on the U.S. economy.

What Causes Globalization: Text

1. **Assess an Argument** In the Middle Ages, merchants traveling along the Silk Road carried not only goods but also ideas. This aspect of globalization is still happening today. Do you agree? Explain.

Challenges of Globalization: Text

2. **Determine Author's Point of View** Kofi Annan, the former UN Secretary General, once said, "Arguing against globalization is like arguing against the laws of gravity." What do you think he meant?

3. **Cite Evidence** Some economists claim that multinational companies have a positive impact on countries in which they set up operations. If you were the spokesperson for an association of multinationals, what evidence would you cite to support this claim?

4. **Support a Point of View With Evidence** Do you think multinational corporations have an obligation to aid the less developed countries in which they operate? Why or why not?

Migration: Text

5. **Identify Cause and Effect** Why does rapid urbanization often bring with it an increase in crime and disease?

Ongoing Issues: Text

6. **Analyze Interactions** Leaders of some less developed countries claim that international trade and financial policies favor the wealthier nations. Assuming that is at least partly true, how do you think such a situation has come about? Why are developed nations in a position to "make the rules"?

7. **Compare and Contrast** Is the goal of sustainable development more attainable by a developed nation or by a less developed country? Explain.

8. **Draw Inferences** Read the following accusation from the past president of Brazil, and then answer the questions below.

   "There are meddlers who have no political authority, who emit carbon dioxide like nobody else, who destroy everything they have, and who put forth opinions about what we should do."

   Who are the "meddlers" to whom Brazil's president refers? How do you know?

9. **Identify Cause and Effect** How does competition for dwindling resources, such as oil, cause prices to rise?

The United States and the Global Economy: Text

10. **Draw Conclusions** Do you think American companies can successfully deal with the pressure to compete and the pressure to innovate and can thus continue to profit in a globalized economy? Explain.